The Exams

This stuff is as dull as dishwater, but you really need to <u>know what you're in for</u>.

Make Sure You Know Which Exam Route You're Doing

1) You'll have to do exams that test your <u>knowledge of Biology</u>, <u>Chemistry</u> and <u>Physics</u>.

2) You <u>also</u> need to know about <u>How Science Works</u>. There's a <u>whole section</u> about it to help you — see pages 2-10. Make sure you understand it <u>all</u> before the exams.

3) You also have to do a <u>Controlled Assessment</u> (also known as an 'ISA') — it's a bit like a <u>coursework exam</u>. See page 11 for more.

4) There are <u>two different exam routes</u> you can take:

<u>ROUTE 1</u>   <u>WHAT YOU NEED TO REVISE FROM THIS BOOK</u>

- Unit 1 exam — Biology 1 ➤ • Sections B1a and B1b
- Unit 2 exam — Chemistry 1 ➤ • Sections C1a and C1b
- Unit 3 exam — Physics 1 ➤ • Sections P1a and P1b
- Controlled Assessment (ISA) ➤ • How Science Works pages 2-11

OR

<u>ROUTE 2</u>   <u>WHAT YOU NEED TO REVISE FROM THIS BOOK</u>

- Unit 5 exam — 1st half of Biology 1, ➤ • Sections B1a, C1a and P1a
  1st half of Chemistry 1,
  1st half of Physics 1
- Unit 6 exam — 2nd half of Biology 1, ➤ • Sections B1b, C1b and P1b
  2nd half of Chemistry 1,
  2nd half of Physics 1
- Controlled Assessment (ISA) ➤ • How Science Works pages 2-11

5) If you don't know which route you're doing <u>ASK YOUR TEACHER</u>, so you revise the <u>RIGHT STUFF</u> for the <u>RIGHT EXAM</u>.

Top Tips for Top Marks in the Exam

1) For some of the <u>long answer questions</u> you'll be marked on your <u>spelling</u>, <u>punctuation</u> and <u>grammar</u>. Remember to write in <u>full sentences</u> and check your work at the end of the exam.

2) <u>Double-check</u> your answer if you've had to <u>calculate</u> something. Write down all your <u>working out</u> and don't forget to include the <u>units</u> either.

3) The examiners expect you to be able to <u>use your knowledge</u> to answer questions about <u>unfamiliar things</u>, e.g. use your knowledge of wave refraction to answer questions about glasses lenses. Don't panic — you should be able to <u>work it out</u> using <u>what you've learnt about the topic</u>.

Exam routes — simpler than bus routes...

Revising for exams is about as exciting as <u>watching paint dry</u>, but it's the only way you'll get <u>good marks</u>. Try to spend a little more time revising the topics you find hard. And make sure you know <u>what you should be revising for each exam</u> — you'll feel a right idiot if you learn the wrong stuff.

The Scientific Process

For your <u>exams</u> and your <u>controlled assessment</u>, you need to know about how the world of science works.

Science is All About Testing Hypotheses

Scientists make an observation.

1) Scientists <u>OBSERVE</u> (look at) something they don't understand, e.g. an illness.
2) They come up with a <u>possible explanation</u> for what they've observed.
3) This explanation is called a <u>HYPOTHESIS</u>.

They test their hypothesis.

4) Next, they test whether the hypothesis is <u>right or not</u>.
5) They do this by making a <u>PREDICTION</u> — a statement based on the hypothesis that can be tested.
6) They then <u>TEST</u> this prediction by carrying out <u>experiments</u>.
7) If their prediction is <u>right</u>, this is <u>EVIDENCE</u> that their <u>hypothesis might be right</u> too.

Other scientists test the explanation too.

8) Other scientists carry out <u>more experiments</u> to test the hypothesis.
9) Sometimes these scientists will find <u>more evidence</u> that the <u>hypothesis is RIGHT</u>.
10) Sometimes they'll find <u>evidence</u> that shows the <u>hypothesis is WRONG</u>.

The explanation is accepted or rejected.

11) If <u>all the evidence</u> that's been found <u>supports</u> the <u>hypothesis</u>, it becomes an <u>ACCEPTED THEORY</u> and goes into <u>textbooks</u> for people to learn.
12) If the <u>evidence</u> shows that the hypothesis is <u>wrong</u>, scientists must:
   • <u>Change the hypothesis</u>, OR
   • Come up with a <u>new hypothesis</u>.

About 100 years ago, we thought atoms looked like this.

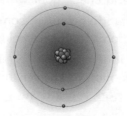

Then we thought they looked like this.

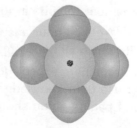

Now we think it's more like this.

<u>You expect me to believe that — then show me the evidence...</u>

If scientists think something is true, they need to produce evidence to convince others — it's all part of <u>testing a hypothesis</u>. Along the way some hypotheses will be <u>disproved</u> (shown not to be true).

Your Data's Got To be Good

Evidence is the key to science — but not all evidence is good...

Lab Experiments and Studies Are Better Than Rumour

1) Laboratory experiments are great. A lab is the easiest place to control the variables in your experiment. This makes it easier to carry out a FAIR TEST.

2) For things that you can't study in a lab (e.g. climate) you carry out scientific studies. In studies, you control as many of the variables as possible.

3) Old wives' tales and rumours are NOT scientific. Without any evidence, they're just opinions.

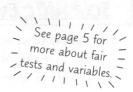
See page 5 for more about fair tests and variables.

The Bigger the Sample Size the Better

1) Sample size is how many things you test in an experiment or study, e.g. 500 people or 20 types of metal.

2) The bigger the sample size the better — to reduce the chance of any weird results.

3) But scientists have to be realistic when choosing how big their sample should be.
E.g. if you were studying how lifestyle affects weight it'd be great to study everyone in the UK (a huge sample), but it'd take ages and cost loads.

Evidence Needs to be Reliable

Reliable evidence comes from experiments that give the same data:

- each time the experiment is repeated
- each time the experiment is reproduced (copied) by other scientists.

> RELIABLE means that the data can be repeated, and reproduced by others.

> EXAMPLE: In 1989, two scientists claimed that they'd produced 'cold fusion' (the energy source of the Sun). Other scientists couldn't get the same results though — they weren't reliable.

Evidence Also Needs to Be Valid

> VALID means that the data is reliable AND answers the original question.

EXAMPLE: DO POWER LINES CAUSE CANCER?
- Some studies have found that in areas where there were power lines, more children had cancer.
- This evidence is NOT enough to say that the power lines CAUSE cancer. Other explanations might be possible, e.g. power lines are often near busy roads, so the areas tested could contain different levels of pollution from traffic.
- So these studies don't show a definite link and so don't answer the original question.

RRRR — Remember, Reliable means Repeatable and Reproducible...

So. Now you know loads about evidence. The fun doesn't stop here though — there's more on the next page.

How Science Works

Bias and Issues Created by Science

It isn't all fun and games in the world of science — there are some problems...

Scientific Evidence can be Biased

1) People who want to make a point can sometimes present data in a biased way — i.e. in a way that's meant to affect how other people think.

2) There are all sorts of reasons why people might want to do this — for example...

- Scientists might want to keep the company that's paying for the research happy. (If the company's not happy they might not pay for any more research.)
- Governments might want to persuade voters to vote for them.
- Companies might want to make their products sound better.

Scientific Developments are Great, but they can Raise Issues

Scientific knowledge increases by doing experiments. This knowledge leads to scientific developments, e.g. new technology or new advice. These developments can create issues though. For example:

Economic (money) issues:

Governments can't always afford to do things scientists recommend, e.g. spend money on green energy sources.

Social (people) issues:

Decisions based on scientific evidence affect people — e.g. should alcohol be banned (to prevent health problems)?

Ethical (moral) issues:

There are a lot of things science has made possible, but should we do them? E.g. clone humans, develop better nuclear weapons.

Environmental issues:

Nuclear power helps us produce more energy — but some people think it causes too many environmental problems.

Some Questions are Unanswered by Science — Some are Unanswerable

1) At the moment scientists don't agree on some things, e.g. what the universe is made of.

2) This is because there isn't enough reliable and valid evidence.

3) But eventually, we probably will be able to answer these questions once and for all.

4) All we need is more evidence.

5) But the question of whether something is ethically right or wrong can't ever be answered by more experiments. There is no "right" or "wrong" answer.

6) The best we can do is make a decision that most people are more or less happy to live by.

CGP make the best revision guides — nope, no bias here...

Spotting biased evidence isn't the easiest thing in the world — ask yourself, 'Will the scientist gain something (or lose something)?' If they might it's possible that the evidence could be biased.

Designing Investigations

You need to know a shed load about <u>investigations</u> for your <u>controlled assessment</u> and <u>all your exams</u>. Investigations include <u>experiments</u> and <u>studies</u>. The next six pages take you from start to finish. Enjoy.

Investigations Produce Evidence to Support or Disprove a Hypothesis

1) When scientists <u>observe</u> something they come up with a <u>hypothesis</u> to explain it (see page 2).

2) To decide whether a hypothesis is correct or not you need to do an <u>investigation</u> to <u>gather some evidence</u>.

3) The first step is to use the hypothesis to come up with a <u>prediction</u> — a statement about what you <u>think will happen</u> that you can <u>test</u>.

Sometimes a hypothesis and a prediction are the same thing.

4) For example, if your <u>hypothesis</u> is:

> "Spots are caused by picking your nose too much."

Then your <u>prediction</u> might be:

> "People who pick their nose more often will have more spots."

5) Investigations are used to see if there are <u>patterns</u> or <u>relationships between two variables</u> (see below).

6) The investigation has to be a <u>FAIR TEST</u> to make sure the evidence is <u>reliable</u> and <u>valid</u>...

See page 3 for more on reliability and validity.

To Make an Investigation a Fair Test You Have to Control the Variables

Investigations that you plan should always be a <u>fair test</u>.

1) In a lab experiment you usually <u>change one thing</u> (a variable) and <u>measure</u> how it affects <u>another thing</u> (another variable).

> EXAMPLE: you might change only the temperature of a reaction and measure how it affects the rate of reaction.

2) <u>Everything else</u> that could affect the results needs to <u>stay the same</u>. Then you know that the thing you're <u>changing</u> is the <u>only</u> thing that's affecting the results.

> EXAMPLE continued: you need to keep the pH the same. If you don't, you won't know if any change in the rate of reaction is caused by the change in temperature, or the change in pH.

3) The variable that you <u>CHANGE</u> is called the <u>INDEPENDENT</u> variable.

4) The variable that's <u>MEASURED</u> is called the <u>DEPENDENT</u> variable.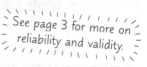

5) The variables that you <u>keep the same</u> are called <u>control</u> variables.

> EXAMPLE continued:
> Independent = temperature
> Dependent = rate of reaction
> Control = pH

Designing Investigations

Trial Runs Help Figure out the Range and Interval of Variable Values

1) A <u>trial run</u> is a <u>quick version</u> of your experiment.

2) Trial runs help you work out whether your plan is <u>right or not</u> — you might decide to make some <u>changes</u> after trying out your method.

3) They're used to figure out the <u>range</u> of values (the highest and lowest value) for the variable you're changing (the independent variable).

4) And they're used to figure out the <u>interval</u> (gaps) between the values too.

> Rate of reaction example from previous page continued:
>
> • You might do trial runs at 10, 20, 30, 40 and 50 °C. If there was no reaction at 10 or 50 °C, you might narrow the range to 20-40 °C.
>
> • If using 10 °C intervals gives you a big change in rate of reaction you might decide to use 5 °C intervals, e.g. 20, 25, 30, 35...

5) Trial runs can also help you figure out <u>how many times</u> the experiment has to be <u>repeated</u> to get reliable results. E.g. if you repeat it three times and the <u>results</u> are all <u>similar</u>, then three repeats is enough.

It Can Be Hard to Control the Variables in a Study

1) You have to <u>control</u> all the <u>variables</u> in a study or it won't be a <u>fair test</u> (just like in a lab experiment).

2) Sometimes though, this is really <u>hard</u> — so you have to use a <u>control group</u> to help.

3) A control group is group of whatever you're studying (e.g. plants) that's kept under the <u>same conditions</u> as the group in the experiment. However, the control group doesn't have anything done to it.

> EXAMPLE:
> • If you're studying the effect of pesticides (pest killer) on plant growth, pesticide is put on one field but not another field (the control field).
> • Both fields contain the same plants and get the same weather conditions.
> • The control field is there so that you can check it's the pesticide causing the results — not the weather.

Investigations Can be Hazardous

1) A <u>hazard</u> is something that <u>could cause harm</u>.

2) Hazards include things like <u>microorganisms</u> (e.g. bacteria), <u>chemicals</u>, <u>electricity</u> and <u>fire</u>.

3) Scientists need to <u>manage the risk</u> of hazards by doing things to reduce them. For example:

> • If you're using a <u>Bunsen burner</u>, stand it on a heat-proof mat.
> • This will reduce the risk of starting a fire.

You won't get a trial run at the exam, so get learnin'...

All this info needs to be firmly lodged in your memory. Learn the <u>names</u> of the different <u>variables</u> — if you remember that the variable you cha**N**ge is called the i**N**dependent variable, you can figure out the other ones.

Collecting Data

It's good if you can design an investigation that people will praise for years to come.
But you'll also need to get your hands mucky and <u>collect some data</u>.

Your Data Should be as Reliable, Accurate and Precise as Possible

1) To make your results more reliable, you should repeat each reading at least <u>three times</u>.
   Then you can calculate the <u>mean</u> (average) — see next page.

2) Checking your results match with <u>secondary sources</u>
   (e.g. other studies) also makes your data more reliable.

3) Your data also needs to be <u>ACCURATE</u>. Accurate results
   are those that are <u>really close</u> to the <u>true answer</u>.

4) Your data also needs to be <u>PRECISE</u>. Precise results
   are ones that are <u>really similar</u> to the <u>mean</u>.

Repeat	Data set 1	Data set 2
1	12	11
2	14	18
3	13	10
Mean	13	13

Data set 1 is more precise
than data set 2.

The Equipment Used has to be Right for the Job

1) You need to make sure you choose the <u>right equipment</u>.

2) For example, the measuring equipment you use has to be able to <u>accurately</u> measure the chemicals
   you're using. If you need to measure out 11 ml of a liquid, use a measuring cylinder that can
   measure to 1 ml, not 5 or 10 ml.

3) The <u>smallest change</u> a measuring instrument can <u>detect</u> is called its <u>RESOLUTION</u>.
   E.g. some mass balances have a resolution of 1 g, some have a resolution of 0.1 g.

4) Equipment needs to be <u>CALIBRATED</u> (set up properly) so that your data is <u>more accurate</u>.
   E.g. mass balances need to be set to zero before you start weighing things.

Errors can Pop Up if You're Not Careful

1) The results of your experiment will always <u>vary a bit</u>.

2) Sometimes, errors will be made. If the <u>same error</u> is made every time, it's called a <u>SYSTEMATIC ERROR</u>.

3) If a systematic error is caused by using <u>equipment</u> that <u>isn't calibrated properly</u> it's called a <u>ZERO ERROR</u>.

Errors can Affect Your Results

1) Sometimes you get a result that <u>doesn't seem to fit in</u>
   with the rest at all.

2) These results are called <u>ANOMALOUS RESULTS</u>.

3) You should investigate them and try to <u>work out what happened</u>.

4) If you can work out what happened (e.g. you measured something
   wrong) you can <u>ignore</u> them when processing your results.

Park	Number of pigeons	Number of crazy tramps
A	28	1
B	42	2
C	1127	0

Anomalous result

Zero error — sounds like a Bruce Willis film...

Weirdly, data can be really <u>precise</u> but <u>not very accurate</u>, e.g. a fancy piece of lab equipment might give results
that are precise, but if it's not calibrated properly those results won't be accurate.

Processing and Presenting Data

The fun doesn't stop once you've collected your data — it then needs to be **processed** and **presented**...

Data Needs to be Organised

1) Data that's been collected needs to be organised so it can be processed later on.

2) Tables are dead useful for organising data.

3) You should always make sure that each column has a heading and that you've included the units.

Test tube	Repeat 1 (ml)	Repeat 2 (ml)	Repeat 3 (ml)
A	28	37	32
B	47	51	60
C	68	72	70

You Might Have to Process Your Data

1) When you've done repeats of an experiment you should always calculate the **MEAN** (average).

2) To calculate the mean **ADD TOGETHER** all the data values. Then **DIVIDE** by the total number of data values.

3) You might also need to calculate the **RANGE** (how spread out the data is).

4) To do this find the **LARGEST** number and **SUBTRACT** the **SMALLEST** number from it.

Ignore anomalous results when calculating these.

EXAMPLE:

Test tube	Repeat 1 (g)	Repeat 2 (g)	Repeat 3 (g)	Mean (g)	Range (g)
A	28	37	32	(28 + 37 + 32) ÷ 3 = 32.3	37 – 28 = 9
B	47	51	60	(47 + 51 + 60) ÷ 3 = 52.7	60 – 47 = 13
C	68	72	70	(68 + 72 + 70) ÷ 3 = 70.0	72 – 68 = 4

If Your Data Comes in Categories, Present it in a Bar Chart

1) If the independent variable comes in clear categories (e.g. blood types, metals) you should use a bar chart to display the data.

2) There are some golden rules you need to follow for drawing bar charts:

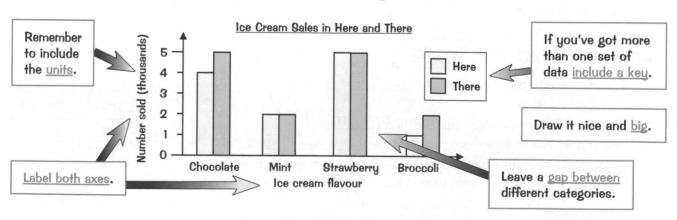

Remember to include the units.

Label both axes.

Ice Cream Sales in Here and There

If you've got more than one set of data include a key.

Draw it nice and big.

Leave a gap between different categories.

Here's a tip from me — never present data as a Mother's Day gift...

Examiners are a bit picky when it comes to bar charts — if you don't draw them properly they won't be happy. Also, **double check** any mean or range **calculations** you do, just to be sure you've got them right.

Presenting Data

Scientists just <u>love</u> presenting data as <u>line graphs</u> (weirdos)...

If Your Data Covers a Range of Values, Plot a Line Graph

If the independent variable can have any value within a range (e.g. length, volume, temperature) you should use a <u>line graph</u> to display the data.

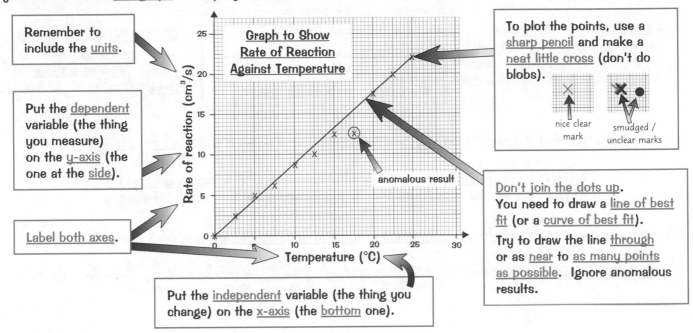

Remember to include the <u>units</u>.

Put the <u>dependent</u> variable (the thing you measure) on the <u>y-axis</u> (the one at the <u>side</u>).

Label both axes.

To plot the points, use a <u>sharp pencil</u> and make a <u>neat little cross</u> (don't do blobs).

nice clear mark

smudged / unclear marks

Don't join the dots up. You need to draw a <u>line of best fit</u> (or a <u>curve of best fit</u>).

Try to draw the line <u>through</u> or as <u>near</u> to <u>as many points as possible</u>. Ignore anomalous results.

Put the <u>independent</u> variable (the thing you change) on the <u>x-axis</u> (the <u>bottom</u> one).

Line Graphs Can Show Patterns in Data

1) Line graphs are used to <u>show the relationship</u> between two variables (just like other graphs).

2) The relationship between two variables is called a <u>CORRELATION</u>:

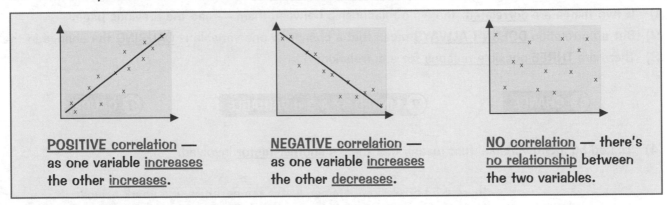

<u>POSITIVE</u> correlation — as one variable <u>increases</u> the other <u>increases</u>.

<u>NEGATIVE</u> correlation — as one variable <u>increases</u> the other <u>decreases</u>.

<u>NO</u> correlation — there's <u>no relationship</u> between the two variables.

3) You need to be able to describe the following patterns on line graphs too:

<u>LINEAR</u> — the graph is a <u>straight line</u>.

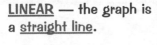
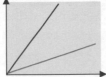

<u>DIRECTLY PROPORTIONAL</u> — the graph is a <u>straight line</u> where both variables increase (or decrease) in the <u>same ratio</u>.

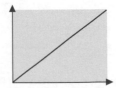

There's a positive correlation between revision and boredom...

...but there's also a positive correlation between <u>revision</u> and getting a <u>better mark in the exam</u>. Cover the page and write down the <u>six things</u> you need to remember when <u>drawing line graphs</u>. No sneaky peeking either — I saw you.

Drawing Conclusions

Congratulations — you've made it to the <u>final step</u> of an investigation — <u>drawing conclusions</u>.

You Can Only Conclude What the Data Shows and NO MORE

1) To come to a conclusion, <u>look at your data</u> and <u>say what pattern you see</u>.

<u>EXAMPLE</u>: The table on the right shows the heights of pea plant seedlings grown for three weeks with different fertilisers.

Fertiliser	Mean growth / mm
A	13.5
B	19.5
No fertiliser	5.5

<u>CONCLUSION</u>: Fertiliser <u>B</u> makes <u>pea plant</u> seedlings grow taller over a <u>three week</u> period than fertiliser A.

2) It's important that the conclusion <u>matches the data</u> it based on — it <u>shouldn't go any further</u>.

<u>EXAMPLE</u> <u>continued</u>: You can't conclude that fertiliser B makes <u>any other type of plant</u> grow taller than fertiliser A — the results could be totally different.

3) You also need to be able to <u>use your results</u> to <u>justify your conclusion</u> (i.e. back it up).

<u>EXAMPLE</u> <u>continued</u>: Fertiliser B made the pea plants grow 6 mm more on average than fertiliser A.

Correlation DOESN'T Always Mean Cause

1) If two things are <u>correlated</u>, there's a relationship between them — see the previous page.
2) But a correlation <u>DOESN'T ALWAYS</u> mean that a change in one variable is <u>CAUSING</u> the change in the other.
3) There are <u>THREE</u> possible reasons for a correlation:

 ① CHANCE  **② LINKED BY A 3rd VARIABLE**   **③ CAUSE**

4) 'Linked by a 3rd variable' just means that there's <u>another factor</u> involved.

E.g. there's a correlation between water temperature and shark attacks. They're linked by a <u>third variable</u> — the number of people swimming (more people swim when the water's hotter, which means you get more shark attacks).

I conclude that this page is a bit dull...

In the exams you could be given a <u>conclusion</u> and asked <u>whether some data supports it</u> — so make sure you understand <u>how far conclusions can go</u>.

Controlled Assessment (ISA)

Controlled Assessment involves <u>answering two question papers</u> under exam conditions — but there's the added bonus of <u>doing an experiment</u> between them. Sounds thrilling.

There are Two Sections in the Controlled Assessment

① Planning

1) Before you sit down to do the Section 1 question paper you'll be given a <u>hypothesis/prediction</u>.

2) You'll then need to <u>research two</u> different methods to test the hypothesis.

3) You'll need to be able to <u>outline both methods</u> and say which one is <u>best</u> (and why it's the best one). Then describe the best method in <u>detail</u>.

4) You're allowed to write <u>notes</u> about your two methods on <u>one side of A4</u> and have them with you for both question papers. Make sure they cover:

- What variables you're going to <u>control</u> (and <u>how</u> you're going to control them).
- What <u>measurements</u> you're going to take.
- How you'd use a <u>trial run</u> to figure out the <u>range</u> and <u>interval</u> you'll use for the <u>independent variable</u>. See page 6 for more.
- What <u>range</u> and <u>interval</u> of values you will use for the <u>independent variable</u>.
- How many times you're going to <u>repeat</u> the experiment — at least <u>three</u> is a good idea.
- What <u>equipment</u> you're going to use (and <u>why</u> that equipment is <u>right for the job</u>).
- <u>How to carry out</u> the experiment, i.e. what you do first, what you do second...
- What <u>hazards</u> are involved in doing the experiment, and <u>how to reduce them</u>.
- What <u>table</u> you'll draw to put your results in. See p.8 for how to draw one that examiners will love.

There's lots of help on all of these things on pages 5-8.

When you've done the planning and completed the first question paper you'll actually <u>do the experiment</u>. Then you'll have to <u>present your data</u>.

After that it's onto the Section 2 question paper...

② Drawing Conclusions and Evaluating

For the Section 2 question paper you have to do these things for <u>your experiment</u>:

1) <u>Draw conclusions</u> from your results. For this you need to <u>describe the relationship</u> between the variables in <u>detail</u> — see the previous page for how to do this.

2) Say whether your results <u>back up the hypothesis/prediction</u>, and give reasons <u>why</u> or <u>why not</u>.

3) <u>Evaluate</u> your experiment. For this you need to <u>suggest ways you could improve your experiment</u>.

- Comment on your <u>equipment</u> and <u>method</u>, e.g. could you have used more <u>accurate</u> equipment?
- Make sure you <u>explain how</u> the improvements would give you <u>better data</u> next time.
- <u>Refer to your results</u>. E.g. 'I could use a more sensitive mass balance next time to work out a more accurate rate of reaction. This could have stopped me from getting the anomalous result in the second repeat of the experiment'.

You'll also be <u>given some secondary data</u> (data collected by other people) from experiments on the same topic and asked to <u>analyse it</u>.

This just involves doing what you did for your data with the secondary data, e.g. draw conclusions from it.

If that's controlled assessment, I'd hate to see uncontrolled assessment...

That might be an Everest-sized list of stuff, but it's <u>all important</u>. No need to panic at the sight of it though — as long as you've <u>learnt everything</u> on the previous few pages, you should be fine.

How Science Works

Diet and Metabolic Rate

The first thing on the GCSE AQA A Core Science menu is... well... <u>food</u>.
It's where you <u>get</u> your <u>energy</u> from, to do all sorts of things like talking, partying and maybe a bit of <u>revision</u>.

A Balanced Diet Keeps You Healthy

1) For good health, your diet must give you the <u>energy</u> you need (but <u>not more</u>).

2) You need to have the right <u>balance</u> of different foods as well.

3) So you need:

...enough <u>carbohydrates</u> to release <u>energy</u>,

...enough <u>fats</u> to <u>keep warm</u> and release <u>energy</u>,

...enough <u>protein</u> to <u>build and repair cells</u>,

...and tiny amounts of various <u>vitamins</u> and <u>mineral ions</u> to keep your skin, bones, blood and everything else generally healthy.

Different People have Different Energy Needs

1) You need <u>energy</u> to fuel the <u>chemical reactions</u> in the body that keep you alive.

2) These reactions are called your <u>metabolism</u>.

3) The <u>speed</u> these reactions happen at is your <u>metabolic rate</u>.

4) Your metabolic rate <u>varies</u> depending on:

1 How much MUSCLE you have

If you have <u>more muscle than fat</u>, you'll need <u>more energy</u>, so you'll have a <u>high metabolic rate</u>.

2 How ACTIVE you are

If you have an <u>active job</u> or <u>exercise</u> lots, you'll need <u>more energy</u>, so you'll have a <u>high metabolic rate</u>.

3 INHERITED FACTORS

<u>Inherited factors</u> (i.e. your genes) can affect your metabolic rate (see page 13).

Diet tip — the harder you revise the more calories you burn...

So basically, eating healthily involves eating the <u>right amount</u> of food and the <u>right type</u> of food. You've also got to eat <u>enough food</u> to match your <u>energy needs</u>... or do enough exercise to match your eating habits. Well, what are you waiting for — time to burn off those calories by <u>revising</u> all of this page.

Factors Affecting Health

Being healthy doesn't just mean you look great in your swimwear — it means being free of any diseases too.

Your Health is Affected by Having an Unbalanced Diet...

1) People whose diet is badly out of balance are said to be <u>malnourished</u>.

2) An <u>unbalanced diet</u> can be where people:

1 EAT TOO MUCH

1) This can lead to a person being <u>overweight</u> or <u>obese</u> (very overweight).

2) It can happen if someone eats too much <u>carbohydrate</u> or <u>fat</u>.

3) Obesity can cause <u>type 2 diabetes</u>, a condition where someone <u>can't control</u> the level of <u>sugar</u> in their blood.

2 EAT TOO LITTLE

1) This can lead to a person being <u>underweight</u>.

2) Not eating enough <u>vitamins</u> or <u>minerals</u> can cause <u>deficiency diseases</u>. E.g. not eating enough <u>vitamin C</u> causes <u>scurvy</u>.

...Not Getting Enough Exercise...

1) People who <u>exercise regularly</u> are usually <u>healthier</u> than those who don't do regular exercise.

2) Exercise <u>increases</u> the amount of <u>energy</u> used by the body and <u>decreases</u> the amount <u>stored</u> as <u>fat</u>.

3) Exercise also <u>builds muscle</u> so it helps to boost your <u>metabolic rate</u> (see page 12).

4) So people who exercise are <u>less likely</u> to suffer from health problems such as <u>obesity</u>.

...and Inherited Factors

Inherited factors can affect a person's:

1 METABOLIC RATE

1) Some people are born with a <u>low metabolic rate</u>, so their cells use <u>less energy</u> than normal.

2) This can cause <u>obesity</u> because they <u>don't burn as much energy</u>.

2 CHOLESTEROL LEVEL

1) <u>Cholesterol</u> is a <u>fatty substance</u> that's needed for good health — it's found in all of your cells.

2) Some inherited factors <u>increase</u> blood cholesterol level, which increases the risk of <u>heart disease</u>.

Obesity is a weighty issue these days...

Your health can really <u>suffer</u> if you regularly eat too much, too little, or miss out on a vital nutrient. Exercise is important as well as diet — regular exercise helps to keep you fit.

Evaluating Food, Lifestyle and Diet

How can you tell if a food product is <u>healthy</u>, or if a <u>claim</u> about a diet is <u>true</u>... Read on to find out.

You Need to be Able to Evaluate Information on Food and Lifestyle

1) In the exam, you may get asked to <u>evaluate</u> (weigh up) <u>information</u> about <u>how food affects health</u>.

2) Don't panic — you just need to use <u>what you know</u> from the <u>past two pages</u> to answer the question.

3) Have a look at the <u>example</u> below:

This food provides more energy, carbohydrate and fat so is less healthy, because eating too much can lead to obesity.

FOOD LABEL 1

Energy	388 kJ
Protein	6 g
Carbohydrate	14 g
of which sugars	6 g
Fat	4.2 g
of which saturates	2.2 g

FOOD LABEL 2

Energy	305 kJ
Protein	3 g
Carbohydrate	9 g
of which sugars	8 g
Fat	2.1 g
of which saturates	0.5 g

4) You might get asked to evaluate information about <u>how lifestyle affects health</u>.

5) Your lifestyle includes <u>what you eat</u> and <u>what you do</u>.

6) For example, a person who eats too much <u>fat</u> and doesn't do much <u>exercise</u> increases their risk of <u>obesity</u>.

Watch Out for Slimming Claims that Aren't Scientifically Proven

1) There are loads of <u>slimming products</u> (e.g. slimming milkshakes) and <u>slimming programmes</u> (e.g. the Atkins Diet™) around.

2) They all claim they'll help you <u>lose weight</u> — but how do you know they work...

3) It's a good idea to <u>look out</u> for <u>these things</u>:

- Is the report a **SCIENTIFIC STUDY**, published in a well-known science journal?
- Was it written by a **QUALIFIED PERSON**, who doesn't work for the people selling the product?
- Did the study ask a **LARGE ENOUGH SAMPLE** of people to give reliable results?
- Have there been **OTHER STUDIES** which have found similar results?

If the answers to these questions are "yes", that's a good sign.
If the answers are "no", then the claim may not be true.

For example, a magazine article saying "<u>Celebrity A</u> has lost <u>x pounds</u> using this diet" <u>doesn't mean much</u>.

4) Really, all you need to do to lose weight is to <u>take in less energy</u> than you <u>use</u>.

5) So diets and slimming products will only work if you...

- eat <u>less fat or carbohydrate</u> (so that you take in less energy), or
- do <u>more exercise</u> (so that you use more energy).

"Brad Pitt says it's great" is NOT scientific proof...

... but if 1000 Brad Pitts (I wish) say it's great, then he could be on to something. You may get an exam question that asks about <u>how lifestyle affects health</u>, so make sure you really <u>know the stuff</u> from pages 12 and 13.

Fighting Disease

Microorganisms that enter the body and cause disease are called pathogens.
Pathogens cause infectious diseases — diseases that can easily spread.

There Are Two Main Types of Pathogen: Bacteria and Viruses

1. Bacteria Are Very Small Living Cells

1) Bacteria reproduce rapidly inside your body.

2) They make you feel ill by: 1) damaging your cells,

2) producing toxins (poisons).

2. Viruses Are Not Cells — They're Much Smaller

1) Viruses copy themselves by invading cells and using the cells' machinery to make tons of copies.

2) The cell will usually then burst, releasing all the new viruses.

3) This cell damage is what makes you feel ill.

Your Body Has a Pretty Good Defence System

1) Your skin, plus hairs and mucus in your respiratory tract (airways) stop nasties getting in.

2) If your skin is cut, tiny bits of cells help your blood clot quickly to stop anything else getting in.

3) But if something does make it through, your immune system kicks in.

4) The most important part of your immune system is the white blood cells.

5) When they come across an invading pathogen, they have three lines of attack:

1. Consuming Them

White blood cells can engulf (surround) the pathogens and digest them.

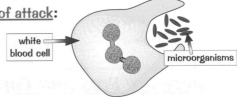

white blood cell

microorganisms

2. Producing Antibodies

1) Every invading pathogen has unique molecules on its surface.

2) These molecules are called antigens.

3) When your white blood cells come across a foreign antigen (i.e. one they don't know), they will start to produce antibodies.

4) Antibodies lock onto and kill the invading pathogens. The antibodies produced are specific to that type of antigen — they won't lock on to any others.

new pathogen

antibodies produced

white blood cell

new pathogens attacked by new antibodies

5) If the person is infected with the same pathogen again, the white blood cells will rapidly produce the antibodies to kill it. The person is naturally immune to that pathogen and won't get ill.

3. Producing Antitoxins

These stop toxins produced by the invading bacteria.

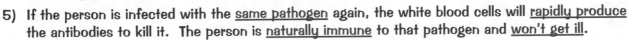

Fight disease — blow your nose with boxing gloves...

Your body is pretty good at defending itself against nasty pathogens. Don't get mixed up between antigens and antibodies — your own body produces antibodies, which lock onto antigens to kill the pathogens.

Fighting Disease — Vaccination

Vaccinations mean we don't always have to treat a disease — we can stop the disease in the first place.

Vaccination — Protects from Future Infections

1) Vaccinations involve injecting small amounts of dead or inactive pathogens into the body.

2) These pathogens have antigens on their surface (see page 15).

3) The antigens cause your white blood cells to produce antibodies to attack the pathogens.

4) If you're infected with the same pathogen later, your white blood cells quickly produce lots of antibodies.

5) These antibodies kill the pathogen so you don't become ill. Cool.

6) For example, the MMR vaccine is used to protect children against the viruses that cause measles, mumps and rubella.

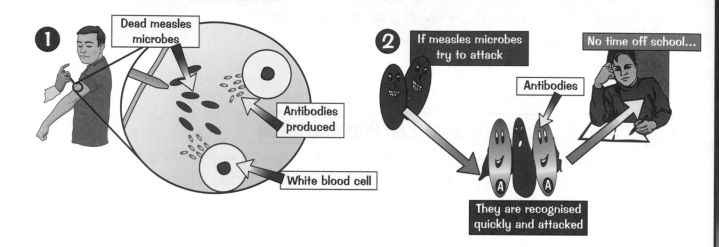

There are Pros and Cons of Vaccination

PROS

❶ Vaccines have helped control lots of infectious diseases that used to be common in the UK, e.g. polio.

❷ 1) A big outbreak of a disease is called an epidemic.
   2) Epidemics can be prevented if lots of people are vaccinated.
   3) That way even the people who aren't vaccinated are unlikely to catch the disease because there are fewer people able to pass it on.

CONS

❶ Vaccines don't always work — sometimes they don't give you immunity.
❷ You can sometimes have a bad reaction to a vaccine, e.g. swelling or a fever.

Prevention is better than cure...

Although vaccinations aren't perfect, it's better to have a vaccine rather than risk catching a nasty disease. No-one wants measles — some people actually die from it. But there aren't vaccines for everything yet. Booo.

Fighting Disease — Drugs

Well knock me down with a feather — it looks like there are even more ways of fighting disease...

Some Drugs Get Rid of Symptoms — Others Cure the Problem

1) Some drugs help to get rid of the symptoms of a disease, e.g. painkillers reduce pain.
2) But these drugs don't kill the pathogens that cause the disease.
3) Antibiotics (e.g. penicillin) kill bacteria.
4) Different antibiotics kill different types of bacteria, so it's important to be treated with the right one.
5) But antibiotics don't destroy viruses (e.g. flu viruses).
6) Viruses reproduce using your own body cells (see page 15).
7) This makes it very difficult to develop drugs that destroy the virus without killing the body's cells.

Bacteria Can Become Resistant to Antibiotics

1) Bacteria can mutate (have changes in their DNA).
2) Some of these mutations cause the bacteria to become resistant to (not killed by) an antibiotic.
3) Resistant strains (types) of bacteria, e.g. MRSA, have increased as a result of natural selection (see p. 41).

You can Investigate Antibiotics by Growing Microorganisms in the Lab

You can test the action of antibiotics or disinfectants by growing microorganisms:

1) Microorganisms are grown in a 'culture medium' (nutrient jelly) in round plastic dishes called Petri dishes.
2) Inoculating loops (wire loops) are used to transfer microorganisms to the jelly.
3) The microorganisms then multiply.
4) Paper discs are soaked in different types of antibiotics and placed on the jelly.
5) Strains of bacteria that are resistant to the antibiotics will keep growing around the discs.
6) Non-resistant strains of bacteria will die.
7) The Petri dishes, culture medium and inoculating loops must be sterilised (cleaned) before use to kill unwanted microorganisms. For example, the inoculating loops are passed through a flame.
8) The Petri dish must also have a lid taped on to stop any microorganisms in the air getting in.
9) In the lab at school, microorganisms are kept at 25 °C so that harmful pathogens won't grow.
10) In industrial conditions they're kept at higher temperatures, so that microorganisms can grow a lot faster.

microorganisms

culture medium (nutrient jelly)

inoculating loop

Bet you can't resist learning this...

Antibiotics were a great discovery. But doctors these days won't give you antibiotics for viral infections like the common cold — because... 1) Antibiotics don't work against viruses. 2) Overuse of antibiotics increases the speed at which resistant strains of bacteria develop. And we don't want that.

Fighting Disease — Past and Future

The treatment of disease has changed over the last 200 years or so.

Semmelweis Cut Deaths by Using Antiseptics

1) A guy called <u>Ignaz Semmelweis</u> worked in a hospital in the 1840s.
2) He saw that lots of women were <u>dying</u> from a disease <u>after giving birth</u>.
3) He believed that <u>doctors</u> were <u>spreading</u> the disease on their <u>unwashed hands</u>.
4) Semmelweis told doctors to <u>wash</u> their hands in an <u>antiseptic solution</u> before seeing patients — and this <u>cut the death rate</u>.
5) The antiseptic solution <u>killed bacteria</u> on doctors' hands (though Semmelweis didn't know this at the time).
6) Now we know that <u>basic hygiene</u> (keeping things <u>clean</u>) is really important to control the spread of disease.

Antibiotic Resistance is Becoming More Common

Remember, antibiotics kill bacteria (see page 17).

1) The number of <u>deaths</u> from bacterial diseases has <u>fallen</u> because of <u>antibiotics</u>.
2) But now there are strains of bacteria that are <u>resistant to antibiotics</u>.
3) We need to <u>slow down</u> the speed at which resistant types develop by <u>not over-using antibiotics</u>.
4) And drug companies are trying to develop <u>new antibiotics</u> that will <u>kill resistant strains</u> of bacteria.

We Face New and Scary Dangers All the Time

BACTERIA

1) Bacteria can <u>mutate</u>, producing <u>new strains</u> (see page 17).
2) A new strain could be <u>antibiotic-resistant</u>, so antibiotics <u>won't work</u>.
3) Or a new strain could be one that we've <u>not come across before</u>, so <u>no-one</u> would be <u>immune</u> to it.
4) This means a new strain of bacteria could <u>spread rapidly</u> in a population of people.
5) It could even cause an <u>epidemic</u> — a big outbreak of disease.

VIRUSES

1) Viruses also tend to <u>mutate often</u>.
2) A mutation can lead to a virus having <u>different antigens</u> (see page 15).
3) If you've been vaccinated your antibodies <u>won't recognise</u> the new antigens, so the <u>vaccine won't work</u>.
4) It's possible that a new virus could <u>spread all over the world</u> — this is called a <u>pandemic</u>.

Don't get your epidemics and pandemics mixed up...

... <u>pandemic</u> contains the word "<u>panic</u>" — you'd certainly panic if there was a worldwide spread of disease. Mind you, you wouldn't sit around twiddling your thumbs if an <u>epidemic</u> turned up at your doorstep either.

The Nervous System

The nervous system allows you to react to what goes on around you — you'd find life tough without it.

Sense Organs Detect Stimuli

A stimulus is a change in your environment which you may need to react to (e.g. a lion charging at you).

1) You have five different sense organs — eyes, ears, nose, tongue and skin.

2) They all contain different receptors.

3) Receptors are groups of cells that detect stimuli.

4) Receptors change stimuli into electrical impulses.

Sense organs and Receptors
Don't get them mixed up:

The eye is a sense organ — it contains light receptors.

The Five Sense Organs and the receptors that each contains:

1) Eyes — Light receptors detect light. These cells have a nucleus, cytoplasm and cell membrane.

2) Ears — Sound receptors detect sound. Also, "balance" receptors detect changes in position.

3) Nose — Smell receptors detect chemical stimuli.

4) Tongue — Taste receptors detect chemical stimuli.

5) Skin — Receptors detect touch, pressure, pain and temperature change.

Sensory Neurones
The nerve cells that carry signals from the receptors to the central nervous system.

Relay Neurones
The nerve cells that carry signals from sensory neurones to motor neurones.

Motor Neurones
The nerve cells that carry signals from the central nervous system to the effector muscles or glands.

Effectors
Muscles contract and glands secrete hormones (see p. 21).

The Central Nervous System Coordinates a Response

1) The central nervous system (CNS) is where all the information from the sense organs is sent, and where responses are coordinated.

2) The central nervous system is made up of the brain and spinal cord.

3) Neurones (nerve cells) transmit the information as electrical impulses.

4) These impulses travel very quickly to and from the CNS.

5) "Instructions" from the CNS are sent to the effectors (muscles and glands), which then respond.

My sound receptors detect rude words when I tell you to revise this...

GCSE Science is a test of how well you can apply what you know. For example, you might have to take what you know about a human and apply it to a horse. Easy... sound receptors in its ears, light receptors in its eyes, etc.

Synapses and Reflexes

Your brain <u>quickly decides</u> how to respond to a stimulus. But <u>reflexes</u> are even quicker...

Synapses Connect Neurones

1) The <u>connection</u> (gap) between <u>two neurones</u> is called a <u>synapse</u>.
2) The nerve signal is taken across the gap by <u>chemicals</u>.
3) These chemicals set off a <u>new electrical signal</u> in the <u>next</u> neurone.

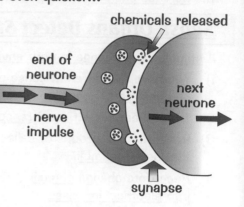

Reflexes Help Prevent Injury

1) <u>Reflexes</u> are <u>automatic responses</u> to certain stimuli — they just happen.
2) Reflexes are much <u>quicker</u> than normal responses because you <u>don't have to think</u> about them.
3) They help to stop you <u>injuring</u> yourself, e.g. <u>bright light</u> makes your <u>pupils smaller</u> to <u>prevent eye damage</u>.

Reflexes Go Through the Central Nervous System

Here's an example...

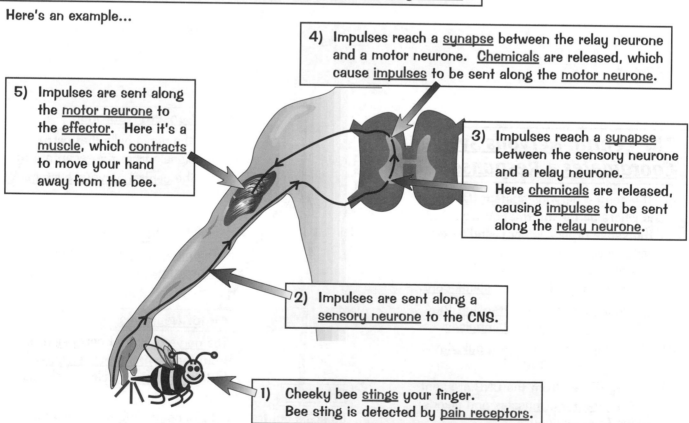

4) Impulses reach a <u>synapse</u> between the relay neurone and a motor neurone. <u>Chemicals</u> are released, which cause <u>impulses</u> to be sent along the <u>motor neurone</u>.

5) Impulses are sent along the <u>motor neurone</u> to the <u>effector</u>. Here it's a <u>muscle</u>, which <u>contracts</u> to move your hand away from the bee.

3) Impulses reach a <u>synapse</u> between the sensory neurone and a relay neurone. Here <u>chemicals</u> are released, causing <u>impulses</u> to be sent along the <u>relay neurone</u>.

2) Impulses are sent along a <u>sensory neurone</u> to the CNS.

1) Cheeky bee <u>stings</u> your finger. Bee sting is detected by <u>pain receptors</u>.

Don't get all twitchy — just learn it...

There are loads of different reflexes. But the good thing is that they all follow the <u>same pathway</u> — so you just need to learn this once. Here it is:

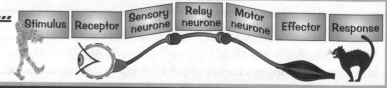

Hormones

The other way to send information around the body (apart from along nerves) is by using <u>hormones</u>.

Hormones Are Chemical Messengers Sent in the Blood

1) <u>Hormones</u> are <u>chemicals</u> released directly into the <u>blood</u>.

2) They're <u>carried</u> in the <u>blood</u> to other parts of the body.

3) Hormones only affect <u>particular cells</u> in particular places (called <u>target cells</u>).

4) Hormones are produced in (and secreted by) various <u>glands</u>, as shown on the diagram.

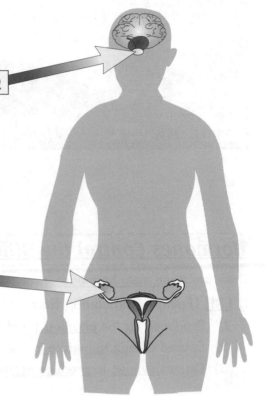

<u>Learn this definition:</u>
HORMONES...
are <u>chemical messengers</u>
which <u>travel in the blood</u>
to <u>activate target cells</u>.

<u>THE PITUITARY GLAND</u>
This produces many
important hormones
including <u>FSH</u> and <u>LH</u>.
They're involved in
the <u>menstrual cycle</u>
(see page 22).

<u>OVARIES</u> — females only
Produce <u>oestrogen</u>, which is
involved in the <u>menstrual cycle</u>
(see page 22).

These are just examples — there are
loads more, each doing its own thing.

Hormones and Nerves Do Similar Jobs, but There Are Differences

<u>NERVES:</u>

1) Very <u>FAST</u> action.
2) Act for a very <u>SHORT TIME</u>.
3) Act on a very <u>PRECISE AREA</u>.

<u>HORMONES:</u>

1) <u>SLOWER</u> action.
2) Act for a <u>LONG TIME</u>.
3) Act in a more <u>GENERAL</u> way.

Oooo errr — hormones...

Hormones control various <u>organs</u> and <u>cells</u> in the body. For example, hormones take care of all things to do with the menstrual cycle, fertility, blood sugar level, ion content, water content... and so on. Pretty amazing really.

The Menstrual Cycle

The menstrual cycle is the monthly release of an egg from a woman's ovaries.
It's also the build-up and breakdown of the protective lining in the uterus (womb).

The Menstrual Cycle Has Four Stages

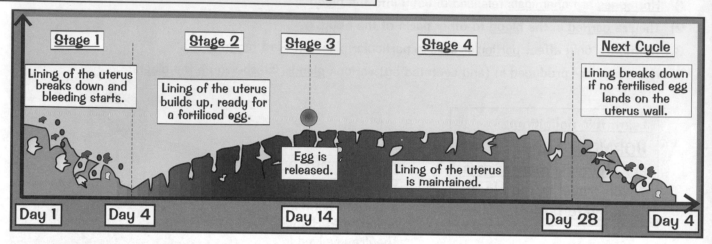

Stage 1 — Lining of the uterus breaks down and bleeding starts.

Stage 2 — Lining of the uterus builds up, ready for a fertilised egg.

Stage 3 — Egg is released.

Stage 4 — Lining of the uterus is maintained.

Next Cycle — Lining breaks down if no fertilised egg lands on the uterus wall.

Day 1   Day 4   Day 14   Day 28   Day 4

Hormones Control the Different Stages

There are three main hormones involved:

1) **FSH** (Follicle-Stimulating Hormone):
   1) Produced by the pituitary gland.
   2) Causes an egg to mature in one of the ovaries.
   3) Causes ovaries to produce oestrogen.

2) **Oestrogen:**
   1) Produced in the ovaries.
   2) Inhibits FSH (stops any more FSH being released).

3) **LH** (Luteinising Hormone):
   Causes the release of an egg from the ovaries.

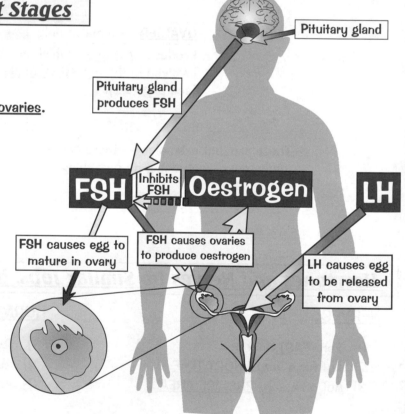

Pituitary gland

Pituitary gland produces FSH

FSH   Inhibits FSH   Oestrogen   LH

FSH causes egg to mature in ovary

FSH causes ovaries to produce oestrogen

LH causes egg to be released from ovary

What do you call a fish with no eye — FSH...

I hope you didn't think you'd get through Biology without having to learn about the menstrual cycle... tough luck.
You need to be sure you know the different hormones involved (FSH, LH and oestrogen) and what they do.
So get out your pen and paper, and scribble scribble scribble till you know all of this page.

Biology 1a — Human Biology

Controlling Fertility

Hormones can be used to <u>change</u> how <u>fertile</u> a woman is (how able she is to have children).

Hormones Can Be Used to Reduce Fertility...

1) <u>Oestrogen</u> reduces fertility because it <u>inhibits FSH</u> (see page 22), so <u>no eggs mature</u>.

2) <u>The pill</u> is an <u>oral contraceptive</u> (a birth-control pill that you swallow).

3) The first version of the pill contained <u>high levels</u> of <u>oestrogen</u> and <u>progesterone</u>.

4) But there were concerns about a <u>link</u> between oestrogen in the pill and <u>side effects</u> like <u>blood clots</u>.

5) The pill now contains <u>lower doses</u> of oestrogen so has <u>fewer side effects</u>.

Progesterone is another hormone that reduces fertility.

PROS	CONS
1) The pill's <u>very effective</u> at preventing pregnancy.	1) There's still a <u>very slight chance</u> of getting pregnant.
2) It <u>reduces</u> the <u>risk</u> of getting some types of <u>cancer</u>.	2) It can cause <u>side effects</u> like headaches.
	3) It <u>doesn't protect</u> against <u>STDs</u> (sexually transmitted diseases).

6) There's also a <u>progesterone-only pill</u> — it has <u>fewer side effects</u> than the pill.

...or Increase It

1) Some women have levels of <u>FSH</u> that are <u>too low</u> to cause their <u>eggs to mature</u>.

2) This means that <u>no eggs</u> are <u>released</u> and the women <u>can't get pregnant</u>.

3) The hormones <u>FSH</u> and <u>LH</u> can be injected by these women to stimulate <u>egg release</u> in their <u>ovaries</u>.

PRO	CONS
It helps a lot of women to <u>get pregnant</u>.	1) It <u>doesn't always work</u>.
	2) It can cause <u>multiple pregnancies</u> (twins etc.).

IVF Can Also Help Couples to Have Children

1) <u>IVF</u> stands for "<u>in vitro fertilisation</u>".

2) It involves giving <u>FSH</u> and <u>LH</u> to a woman to <u>stimulate egg production</u>.

3) Then the <u>eggs</u> are collected from the woman's ovaries and fertilised in a <u>lab</u> using the man's <u>sperm</u>.

4) The fertilised eggs are then grown into <u>embryos</u>.

5) Once the embryos are <u>tiny balls of cells</u>, one or two of them are <u>transferred</u> to the woman's uterus (womb).

PRO	CONS
It can give an infertile couple <u>a child</u>.	1) Some women have a strong <u>reaction</u> to the hormones — e.g. <u>vomiting</u>.
	2) <u>Multiple births</u> can happen — these are <u>risky</u> for the mother and babies.

Different hormones — VERY different effects...

You need to know all the <u>facts</u> and all the <u>issues</u> here. Probably the best way to be sure you know it <u>all</u> is to cover the page, jot down what you know and then check it. Don't worry if you miss bits out, have <u>another go</u>.

Plant Hormones

You may not have expected <u>plants</u> to turn up in a human biology section... but hey, plants have hormones too.

Auxin is a Plant Growth Hormone

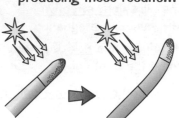

1) <u>Auxin</u> is a <u>plant hormone</u> that controls <u>growth</u>.
2) It controls the growth of a plant in response to <u>LIGHT</u> (<u>phototropism</u>), <u>GRAVITY</u> (<u>gravitropism</u> or <u>geotropism</u>) and <u>MOISTURE</u>.
3) Auxin is made in the <u>tips</u> of shoots and roots.
4) It <u>moves backwards</u> to make the cells <u>just behind</u> the tips grow longer.
5) If the tip of a shoot is <u>removed</u>, no auxin is made and the shoot may <u>stop growing</u>.
6) Auxin <u>increases</u> growth in the <u>shoot</u> but <u>slows</u> growth in the <u>root</u> — producing these results...

Shoots grow towards light

1) When a <u>shoot tip</u> is exposed to <u>light</u>, <u>more auxin</u> builds up on the side that's in the <u>shade</u> than the side that's in the light.
2) This makes the cells grow <u>faster</u> on the <u>shaded side</u>, so the shoot bends <u>towards</u> the light.

Shoots grow away from gravity

1) When a <u>shoot</u> is growing sideways, gravity makes <u>more auxin</u> build up on the <u>lower side</u> of the tip.
2) So the lower side grows <u>faster</u>, bending the shoot <u>upwards</u>.

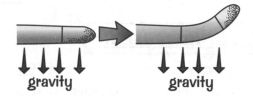

gravity   gravity

Roots grow towards gravity

1) A <u>root</u> growing sideways also has more auxin on its <u>lower side</u>.
2) But in a root the <u>extra</u> auxin <u>slows</u> growth. This means the cells on <u>top</u> grow faster, and the root bends <u>downwards</u>.

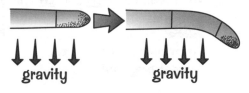

gravity   gravity

Roots grow towards moisture

1) <u>More auxin</u> builds up on the side of a root that has <u>more moisture</u>.
2) This <u>slows</u> growth on that side, causing the root to bend <u>towards the moisture</u>.

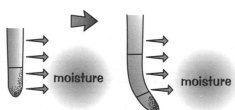

moisture   moisture

Plant Hormones have Uses in Agriculture

1 <u>WEEDKILLERS</u> — some plant growth hormones kill <u>broad-leaved</u> plants like <u>weeds</u>, but <u>narrow-leaved crops aren't harmed</u> (woohoo).

2 <u>ROOTING HORMONES</u> — plant cuttings won't always grow in soil but if you add <u>rooting powder</u>, with <u>auxin</u> in, it <u>helps roots grow</u>.

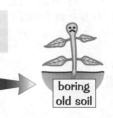

boring old soil

rooting compound

A plant auxin to a bar — 'ouch'...

Learn the page. Learn the <u>whole darn page</u>. There's no getting out of it folks.

Homeostasis

<u>Homeostasis</u> is a fancy word, but it covers lots of things, so maybe that's fair enough.
It means all the functions of your body which try to maintain a "<u>constant internal environment</u>".

Your Body Needs Some Things to Be Kept Constant

1) To keep all your <u>cells working properly</u>, certain things must be <u>kept at the right level</u>.

2) Your body needs to control the levels of the <u>four</u> things below.

(1) Ions

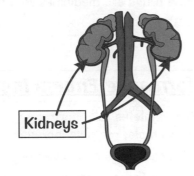

Kidneys

1) <u>Ions</u> (e.g. sodium ions) are taken into the body in <u>food</u>.

2) Some ions are <u>lost</u> in <u>sweat</u>.

3) If your body has <u>more ions</u> than it needs,
   they're <u>removed</u> by the <u>kidneys</u> and got rid of in <u>urine</u>.

(2) Water

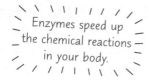

1) Water is <u>taken into</u> the body in <u>food and drink</u>.

2) It's <u>lost</u> from the body in these ways:

    1) through the <u>skin</u> as <u>sweat</u>...

    2) via the <u>lungs</u> in <u>breath</u>...

    3) via the kidneys as <u>urine</u>.

On a <u>COLD DAY</u> you <u>don't sweat much</u>, so you'll produce <u>more urine</u>.

On a <u>HOT DAY</u> you <u>sweat a lot</u>, so you'll produce <u>less urine</u>.

(3) Temperature

1) The <u>enzymes</u> in your body <u>work best</u> at about <u>37 °C</u>.

2) So your body tries to keep itself around this temperature.

Enzymes speed up the chemical reactions in your body.

(4) Blood Sugar

1) Eating foods containing <u>carbohydrate</u> puts <u>sugar</u> into the blood from the <u>gut</u>.

2) The sugar is <u>removed</u> from the blood by all your <u>cells</u>, which use the sugar for <u>energy</u>.

3) Your blood sugar is kept at a <u>steady level</u> so that your cells get a <u>constant supply</u> of <u>energy</u>.

My sister never goes out — she's got homeostasis...

Try <u>spelling</u> 'homeostasis' without looking. Got it — good. Once you can spell it (homeostasis, not 'it')
you need to learn the <u>four things</u> your body keeps constant: <u>ions</u>, <u>water</u>, <u>temperature</u> and <u>blood sugar</u>.

Drugs

Drugs alter the chemical reactions in your body — sometimes for the better, sometimes not.

Drugs Change Your Body Chemistry

1) The chemical changes caused by a drug can make people become addicted to it (want it really badly).
E.g. heroin and cocaine are very addictive.

2) If the drug isn't taken, an addict can suffer withdrawal symptoms — these are often pretty unpleasant.

3) Some drugs are medicines that may be prescribed by a doctor, or got over the counter (non-prescribed).

Performance-Enhancing Drugs have Health and Ethical Impacts

1) Some athletes take performance-enhancing drugs to make them better at sport.
For example, steroids increase muscle size and stimulants increase heart rate.

2) But these drugs can have negative health effects, e.g. steroids can cause high blood pressure.

3) Some of these drugs are banned by law, some are prescription-only, but all are banned by sporting bodies.

4) There are also ethical problems with taking them:

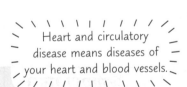

Against drugs...	For drugs...
1) It's unfair if people gain an advantage by taking drugs.	1) Drug-free sport isn't really fair anyway, e.g. athletes may have different coaches.
2) Athletes may not know the health risks.	2) Athletes have the right to make their own decision about whether taking drugs is worth the risk or not.

Claims About Drugs need to be Carefully Looked At

Heart and circulatory disease means diseases of your heart and blood vessels.

E.g. STATINS

1) Statins are a type of prescribed drug.
2) They're used to lower the risk of heart and circulatory disease.
3) There's evidence that statins lower blood cholesterol and lower the risk of heart disease in diabetics.
4) The original research for this was good because:
   - It was done by government scientists with no connection to the manufacturers.
   - The sample was big — 6000 patients.
   - The study compared patients who had taken statins with those who hadn't.
4) Other studies have backed up these findings.

E.g. CANNABIS

1) Cannabis is an illegal drug.
2) Scientists have looked at whether the chemicals in cannabis smoke cause mental health problems.
3) The results vary, so they're still not sure.

Drugs can kill you or cure you (or anything in between)...

Many people take drugs of some kind, e.g. caffeine in coffee. This can be OK if you're careful and don't go mad.
It's misuse that can get you into trouble (e.g. a paracetamol overdose can kill you). Always read the packet.

Testing Medicinal Drugs

<u>New drugs</u> are always being <u>developed</u>. But before they can be given to the general public, they have to go through lots of <u>thorough testing</u>. This is what usually happens...

There are Three Main Stages in Drug Testing

1 Drugs are tested on <u>human cells and tissues</u> in the lab.

2
1) The next step is to test the drug on <u>live animals</u>.
2) This is to see whether the drug <u>works</u> and to find out about its <u>toxicity</u> (how harmful it is).
3) It's also to find the best <u>dosage</u> — the dose at which it's most effective (works best).

3
1) If the drug <u>passes</u> the tests on animals then it's tested on <u>human volunteers</u> in a <u>clinical trial</u>.
2) First, the drug is tested on <u>healthy</u> volunteers.
3) At the start of the trial, a <u>very low dose</u> of the drug is given and this is <u>slowly increased</u>.
4) If the results of the tests on healthy volunteers are <u>good</u>, the drug can be tested on <u>patients</u>.
5) The <u>optimum dose</u> is found. This is the dose of drug that's <u>most effective</u> and has <u>few side effects</u>.
6) To test how well the drug works, patients are put into <u>two groups</u>...

Group 1 is given the <u>new drug</u>. | Group 2 is given a <u>placebo</u> (a substance that's like the drug being tested but doesn't do anything).

7) The doctor <u>compares</u> the two groups of patients to see the <u>actual difference</u> the drug makes.
8) Clinical trials are <u>blind</u> — the patient <u>doesn't know</u> whether they're getting the <u>drug</u> or the <u>placebo</u>.
9) In fact, they're often <u>double-blind</u> — neither the patient nor the <u>doctor</u> knows who's taken the drug and who's taken the placebo until <u>all the results</u> have been gathered.

Things Have Gone Wrong in the Past

1) <u>Thalidomide</u> is a drug that was developed as a <u>sleeping pill</u>.
2) Later it was also found to be good at relieving <u>morning sickness</u> in pregnant women.
3) But thalidomide <u>hadn't been tested</u> as a drug for morning sickness.
4) So it wasn't known that thalidomide could affect the <u>unborn baby</u> and cause <u>arm and leg problems</u>. E.g. some babies were born with very short arms and legs.
5) Thalidomide was <u>banned</u>, and stricter testing procedures were introduced.
6) More recently, thalidomide has been used in the treatment of <u>leprosy</u> and <u>other diseases</u>.

A little learning is a dangerous thing...

Thalidomide is an example of a drug that was developed to try to <u>improve</u> people's lives... but it ended up causing some <u>tragic</u> effects. Could the same thing happen <u>today</u>? Well, maybe not the exact same thing, but there's no such thing as <u>perfect</u> knowledge — we're learning all the time, and you can never get rid of risk <u>completely</u>.

Recreational Drugs

Not all drugs are used by people with illnesses — some are just used for <u>fun</u>. But fun comes with <u>risk</u>. Everyone knows that. Just like the time I thought it'd be fun to roller skate around the office. Hmmm.

Recreational Drugs Can Be Illegal or Legal

1) <u>Illegal</u> drugs are often divided into two main classes — <u>soft</u> and <u>hard</u>.

2) Hard drugs are generally more <u>harmful</u>, but soft drugs can be harmful too. E.g. <u>heroin</u> and <u>ecstasy</u> (hard drugs), and <u>cannabis</u> (a soft drug) can all cause <u>heart</u> and <u>circulatory system</u> problems.

There Are Various Reasons Why People Use Recreational Drugs

1) So if all these recreational drugs are so dangerous, why do so many people use them...

2) When asked why they use cannabis, most users say they <u>enjoy</u> it, it <u>relaxes</u> them or it gets rid of <u>stress</u>.

3) But there may be other reasons too, e.g. <u>problems</u> in someone's <u>personal life</u>.

Some Studies Link Cannabis and Hard Drug Use — Others Don't

1) Almost all users of <u>hard drugs</u> have tried <u>cannabis</u> first.

2) The <u>link</u> between cannabis and hard drugs isn't clear, but <u>three</u> opinions are common...

Cannabis is a "stepping stone":	Cannabis is a "gateway drug":	It's all down to genetics:
The effects of cannabis create a desire to try harder drugs.	Cannabis use brings people into contact with drug dealers.	Certain people are more likely to take drugs generally, so cannabis users will also try other drugs.

Some Legal Drugs have More of an Impact than Illegal Drugs

1) <u>Tobacco</u> and <u>alcohol</u> are both <u>legal</u> recreational drugs.

2) They have a much <u>bigger impact</u> in the UK than illegal drugs, as <u>so many</u> people take them.

SMOKING causes:	ALCOHOL causes:
• <u>lung disease</u> • <u>cancer</u> • <u>addiction</u> (to <u>nicotine</u>)	• <u>slower reactions</u> and <u>poor coordination</u> • <u>liver disease</u> • <u>addiction</u>

3) It <u>costs the NHS loads</u> to <u>treat</u> the effects of tobacco and alcohol.

4) The <u>cost</u> of people being <u>too ill to work</u> also has a big impact on the <u>economy</u>.

5) The <u>crimes</u> committed due to alcohol (e.g. fights, damaging property) take up <u>police time</u> and <u>cost a lot</u>.

Drinking and smoking — it's so big and clever...

So overall, it's the drugs that are <u>legal</u> that have the biggest impact on people and society. Some legal drugs are prescribed by doctors — but these can also have a big impact on <u>health</u> if people <u>misuse</u> them. E.g. people can become addicted to prescribed <u>painkillers</u> if they're overused.

Revision Summary for Biology 1a

Congratulations, you've made it to the end of the first section. I reckon that section wasn't too bad. There's some pretty interesting stuff there — diets, vaccinations, nerves, drugs, booze... what more could you want? Actually, I know what more you could want, some questions to make sure you know it all.

1) Name all the food groups you should eat to have a balanced diet.

2)* Who do you think would have a higher metabolic rate: a secretary or a professional runner?

3) Name one health problem that is linked to obesity.

4) In terms of energy, what does a person have to do to lose weight?

5) Give one way that your immune system defends the body against disease.

6) Describe how the MMR vaccine prevents you getting measles, mumps or rubella.

7) Name one type of bacteria that has developed resistance to antibiotics.

8) What practice did Semmelweis introduce in the 1840s?

9) Where would you find the following receptors in a dog: a) smell
                                                             b) taste
                                                             c) light?

10) What is a synapse?

11) Why do we have reflexes?

12) Define "hormone".

13)* Here's a table of data about response times.
     a) Which response (A or B) is carried by nerves?
     b) Which is carried by hormones?

Response	Reaction time (s)	Length of response (s)
A	0.005	0.05
B	2	10

14) Describe two effects of FSH on the body.

15) State one advantage and one disadvantage of using the contraceptive pill.

16) Briefly describe how IVF is carried out.

17) What is auxin?

18) Name four things that your body needs to keep at a steady level by homeostasis.

19) Give one reason why an athlete might use performance-enhancing drugs like steroids.

20) What is a double-blind drug trial?

21) Name a drug that was not tested thoroughly enough.

22) Describe one opinion about the link between cannabis and hard drug use.

23) Which has the bigger impact on society in the UK, legal or illegal drugs?

* Answers on page 108.

Adaptations

Organisms survive in many <u>different environments</u> because they have <u>adapted</u> to them. That means they have <u>special features</u> that <u>suit</u> the place they live.

Desert Animals Need to Lose Heat

1) Desert animals have very <u>thin layers</u> of <u>body fat</u> to help them <u>lose</u> heat.
2) They also have a <u>thin coat</u> to help them <u>lose</u> heat.
3) They have a <u>large surface area</u> compared to their <u>volume</u> which also helps them <u>lose heat</u>.
4) A <u>sandy colour</u> gives them <u>good camouflage</u> meaning they aren't easy to <u>see</u> — to help them <u>avoid predators</u>, or <u>sneak up on prey</u>.

Arctic Animals Need to Save Heat

1) Arctic animals have a thick layer of <u>body fat</u> for <u>insulation</u> (to keep warm).
2) They also have <u>thick hairy coats</u> to <u>keep body heat in</u>.
3) They have a <u>small surface area</u> compared to their <u>volume</u> — this <u>reduces heat loss</u>.
4) Arctic animals have <u>white fur</u> for <u>camouflage</u>.

Desert Plants Need to Save Water...

...for example, <u>cacti</u> have many features to help them <u>save water</u>:
1) They <u>store water</u> in their <u>thick stem</u>.
2) They have <u>spines instead of leaves</u>, giving them a <u>small surface area</u> — to <u>reduce water loss</u>.
3) Their <u>roots</u> spread out over a <u>large area</u> to <u>absorb water quickly</u>.

Some Plants and Animals Scare Away Predators

Some animals and plants have <u>special features</u> to <u>stop</u> them from being <u>eaten</u>. For example:
1) <u>Thorns</u> on roses.
2) <u>Poisons</u> on bee stings and poison ivy.
3) <u>Warning colours</u> on wasps.

Some Microorganisms Can Live in Extreme Places

1) <u>Extremophiles</u> (a type of microorganism) live in <u>extreme conditions</u>.
2) Examples are super <u>hot</u> volcanic vents, very <u>salty</u> lakes, or at <u>high pressure</u> on the sea bed.

Dessert plants need to taste sweet...

By looking at an animal or plant's <u>features</u>, you should be able to guess at the kind of <u>environment</u> it lives in.
E.g. an elephant has <u>huge ears</u> that <u>lose heat</u>, so it must live in a <u>hot</u> environment.

Competition and Environmental Change

If the environment changes, an organism might not have the things it needs to survive.

Organisms Compete for Resources to Survive

1) <u>Resources</u> are things organisms need from their <u>environment</u> and from <u>other organisms</u> to <u>live</u> and <u>breed</u>:

PLANTS NEED:
1) <u>light</u>
2) <u>space</u>
3) <u>water</u>
4) <u>nutrients</u> from the soil

ANIMALS NEED:
1) <u>space (territory)</u>
2) <u>food</u>
3) <u>mates</u>

2) Organisms <u>compete with other species</u> (and members of their own species) for the <u>same resources</u>.

Environmental Changes are Caused by Different Things

1) The <u>environment</u> in which plants and animals live <u>changes all the time</u>.

2) These changes are caused by <u>living</u> and <u>non-living</u> factors such as:

LIVING FACTORS   More or less:
1) <u>infectious diseases</u>
2) <u>predators</u>
3) <u>prey</u> or <u>food</u>
4) <u>competitors</u> (other organisms that need the same things)

NON-LIVING FACTORS   An increase or decrease in:
1) average <u>temperature</u>
2) average <u>rainfall</u>

Environmental Changes Affect Populations in Three Ways

1) Population SIZE INCREASES

E.g. if the number of <u>prey increases</u>, then there's <u>more food</u> for predators and their numbers <u>increase</u> too.

2) Population SIZE DECREASES

E.g. the number of bees in the USA is <u>falling rapidly</u>. It could be because:
1) <u>Pesticides</u> may be harming bees.
2) There's <u>less food</u> available.
3) There's <u>more disease</u>.

3) Population DISTRIBUTION CHANGES   A change in distribution means a change in <u>where</u> an organism <u>lives</u>.

E.g. the <u>distribution</u> of <u>bird species</u> in <u>Germany</u> is changing because of a <u>rise</u> in average <u>temperature</u>.

I compete with my brother for the front seat of the car...

In the exam you might be given some <u>data</u> and asked about the change in distribution of <u>any</u> organism. Don't panic. Think about what the organism needs to <u>survive</u> and any <u>environmental changes</u> that have happened.

Measuring Environmental Change

It's difficult to <u>measure accurately</u> just how much our environment is changing.
But there are some <u>useful indicators</u> that can be used...

Environmental Changes can be Measured Using Living Indicators...

1) Some <u>organisms</u> are very <u>sensitive to changes</u> in their environment e.g. they <u>can't live</u> in some conditions.

2) These organisms are <u>indicator species</u>.

LOTS OF LICHEN = CLEAN AIR

1) <u>Sulfur dioxide</u> pollution comes from <u>cars</u> and <u>power stations</u>.

2) <u>Lichens can't live</u> where there's <u>lots</u> of <u>sulfur dioxide</u> in the air.

3) So if there are <u>lots of lichen</u> around, the air is <u>clean</u>.

Mayfly larvae and sludgeworms are invertebrates.

MAYFLY LARVAE = CLEAN WATER

1) <u>Sewage</u> in a <u>river</u> leads to <u>less oxygen</u> in the water.

2) <u>Mayfly larvae can't live</u> where there's <u>not much oxygen</u> in the water.

3) So if you find <u>mayfly larvae</u> in a river, the <u>water is clean</u>.

SLUDGEWORMS = POLLUTED WATER

1) <u>Sludgeworms live</u> in water <u>without much oxygen</u>.

2) So if you find <u>sludgeworms</u> in a river, the <u>water is dirty</u>.

...and Non-Living Indicators

1) Scientists use <u>satellites</u> to measure the <u>temperature</u> of the <u>sea surface</u>.

2) They measure <u>rainfall</u> using <u>rain gauges</u>, to find out how much
the average rainfall changes <u>year on year</u>.

3) They use <u>dissolved oxygen meters</u> to
measure <u>how much oxygen</u> there is in water.
E.g. <u>not much oxygen</u> in the water means it's <u>polluted</u>.

Teenagers are an indicator species — not found in clean rooms...

Recording <u>living</u> and <u>non-living</u> things helps scientists to have a good idea of how our environment is changing.
In your exam, you might be given some <u>data</u> about lichen or mayfly larvae as a <u>measure</u> of pollution — you'll
need to work out what the data means. (Easy — lots of lichen means clean air, mayfly larvae mean clean water.)

Pyramids of Biomass

A pyramid of biomass is a <u>diagram</u> that helps us to <u>understand</u> what's going on in a <u>food chain</u>.

You Need to Be Able to Draw Pyramids of Biomass

1) There's <u>less energy</u> and <u>less biomass</u> every time you move <u>up</u> a level in a food chain:

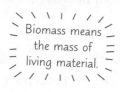

Biomass means the mass of living material.

less energy and biomass   less energy and biomass

<u>100</u> dandelions... feed... <u>10</u> rabbits... which feed... <u>one</u> fox.

2) You can draw a <u>pyramid of biomass</u> to represent the food chain.
3) <u>Each bar</u> shows how much <u>all the organisms</u> at <u>each level</u> would "<u>weigh</u>" if you put them <u>all together</u>.
4) Biomass pyramids are nearly <u>always pyramid-shaped</u>.

fox
rabbits
dandelions

Biomass decreases

You Need to be Able to Interpret Pyramids of Biomass

You need to be able to look at pyramids of biomass and <u>explain</u> what they show about a <u>food chain</u>, e.g.:

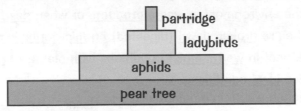

partridge
ladybirds
aphids
pear tree

1) Even if you know nothing about the natural world, you probably know that a <u>tree</u> is <u>bigger</u> than an <u>aphid</u>.
2) So <u>lots</u> (probably thousands) of tiny aphids are feeding on a <u>few</u> great big trees.
3) Quite a lot of <u>ladybirds</u> are then eating the aphids.
4) And a few <u>partridges</u> are eating the ladybirds.
5) The <u>pear trees</u> have the <u>largest biomass</u>.
6) <u>Biomass</u> and <u>energy</u> are <u>decreasing</u> as you go up the levels.

Making pyramids is a breeze — just ask the Egyptians...

Try to remember the most important thing about biomass pyramids — <u>energy</u> and <u>biomass decrease</u> as you go <u>up</u>.

Energy Transfer and Decay

So now you need to learn <u>why</u> there's <u>less energy</u> and <u>biomass</u> each time you move up a level.

All That Energy Just Disappears Somehow...

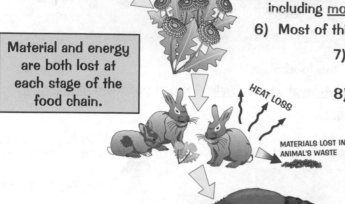

1) Energy from the <u>Sun</u> is the source of energy for <u>nearly all</u> life on Earth.

2) <u>Green plants</u> and <u>algae</u> use a small amount of the light energy from the Sun to make <u>food</u> — this is called <u>photosynthesis</u>.

3) This energy's <u>stored</u> in the cells of plants and algae.

4) The energy goes through the food chain as animals <u>eat</u> plants and other animals.

5) <u>Respiration</u> supplies (releases) the energy for all life processes, including <u>movement</u>.

6) Most of this energy is eventually <u>lost</u> to the surroundings as <u>heat</u>.

7) <u>Material</u> and <u>energy</u> are also lost from the food chain in the organisms' <u>waste materials</u>.

8) This explains why you get <u>biomass pyramids</u>. Most of the biomass is lost and so does <u>not</u> become biomass in the <u>next level up</u>.

> Material and energy are both lost at each stage of the food chain.

HEAT LOSS

MATERIALS LOST IN ANIMAL'S WASTE

Materials are Returned to the Environment by Decay

1) <u>Living things</u> are made of <u>materials</u> they <u>take</u> from the world around them.

2) Materials are <u>returned</u> to the environment in <u>waste products</u> or when <u>dead</u> organisms <u>decay</u>.

3) Materials decay because they're <u>broken down</u> (digested) by <u>microorganisms</u>.

4) Most microorganisms work best in <u>warm</u>, <u>moist</u> conditions with plenty of <u>oxygen</u>.

5) <u>Compost bins</u> recreate these <u>ideal conditions</u>. (Microorganisms decay kitchen waste in a <u>compost bin</u>.)

6) So all the important <u>materials</u> are <u>recycled</u> — they return to the soil, ready to be <u>used</u> by <u>plants</u>.

7) In a <u>stable community</u> the materials <u>taken out</u> of the soil are <u>balanced</u> by those that are put <u>back in</u> — there's a constant <u>cycle</u> happening.

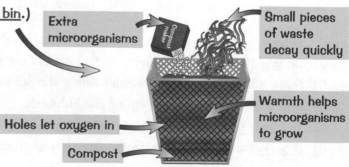

Extra microorganisms

Small pieces of waste decay quickly

Warmth helps microorganisms to grow

Holes let oxygen in

Compost

So when revising, put the fire on and don't take toilet breaks...

No, I'm being silly, go if you have to. But do your bit on the way — put your <u>kitchen waste</u> in the <u>compost</u> and your <u>garden waste</u> (e.g. hedge trimmings) into a <u>green bin</u> (then the council can do the composting for you).

The Carbon Cycle

As you've seen, all the <u>nutrients</u> in our environment are constantly being <u>recycled</u> — there's a nice balance between what <u>goes in</u> and what <u>goes out</u> again. This page is all about the recycling of <u>carbon</u>.

The Carbon Cycle Shows How Carbon is Recycled

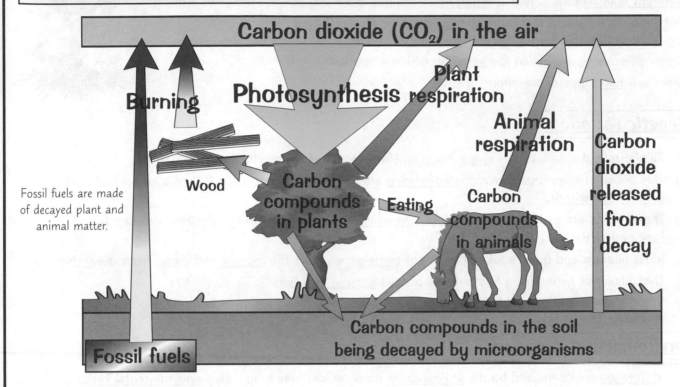

Carbon dioxide (CO_2) in the air

Burning

Photosynthesis

Plant respiration

Animal respiration

Carbon dioxide released from decay

Wood

Fossil fuels are made of decayed plant and animal matter.

Carbon compounds in plants

Eating

Carbon compounds in animals

Fossil fuels

Carbon compounds in the soil being decayed by microorganisms

The <u>energy</u> that plants get from photosynthesis passes up the food chain.

Learn these points:

1) <u>Carbon dioxide</u> is removed from the <u>air</u> by green plants and algae during <u>photosynthesis</u>.
2) The plants and algae use the <u>carbon</u> to make <u>carbohydrates</u>, <u>fats</u> and <u>proteins</u>.
3) Some of the carbon is <u>returned</u> to the air as carbon dioxide when the <u>plants and algae respire</u>.
4) Some of the carbon becomes part of the <u>fats</u> and <u>proteins</u> in <u>animals</u> when the plants and algae are <u>eaten</u>.
5) The carbon then moves through the <u>food chain</u>.
6) Some of the carbon is <u>returned</u> to the air as carbon dioxide when the <u>animals respire</u>.
7) When plants, algae and animals <u>die</u>, <u>microorganisms</u> and <u>detritus feeders</u> feed on them.
8) When these organisms <u>respire</u>, carbon dioxide is <u>returned</u> to the air.
9) Animals also produce <u>waste</u>, which is broken down by <u>detritus feeders</u> and <u>microorganisms</u>.
10) Compounds in the waste are taken up from the <u>soil</u> by plants as <u>nutrients</u> and go back into the <u>food chain</u>.
11) When wood and fossil fuels are <u>burnt</u> (<u>combustion</u>) this <u>releases carbon dioxide</u> back into the air.

Detritus feeders (e.g. worms) are just animals that eat dead organisms.

<u>What goes around comes around...</u>

Carbon is very <u>important</u> for living things — it's the basis for all the chemicals like fats, proteins, carbohydrates, etc. in our bodies. In sci-fi films the aliens aren't always <u>carbon-based</u> — but then by the end they've usually been defeated by some Bruce Willis type, so I don't really think they're onto a winner.

Variation

You'll probably have noticed that not everyone's the same. There are reasons for this.

There Are Differences Within Species

1) <u>Different species</u> look... well... <u>different</u> — my dog definitely doesn't look like a daisy.
2) But even organisms of the <u>same species</u> will look a bit <u>different</u> e.g. different people have <u>different hair colour</u>.
3) These differences are called the <u>variation</u> within a species.
4) There are <u>two</u> types of variation:

① Genetic Variation

1) All plants and animals have <u>characteristics</u> (features) that are similar to their <u>parents</u>'.
2) This is because an organism's <u>characteristics</u> are controlled by <u>genes</u> (p.37) passed on from their <u>parents</u> (<u>inherited</u>).
3) These genes are passed on in <u>sex cells</u> (<u>gametes</u>), which the offspring (children) develop from (see page 38).
4) Most animals and quite a lot of plants get <u>some</u> genes from the <u>mother</u> and <u>some</u> from the <u>father</u>.
5) This mixing of genes from two parents causes <u>genetic variation</u>.
6) <u>Some</u> characteristics are determined <u>only</u> by genes, e.g. <u>blood group</u> in humans.

② Environmental Variation

<u>Any difference</u> that's caused by the <u>environment</u> an organism lives in is called <u>environmental variation</u>.

Example:

1) A plant grown on a nice sunny windowsill would grow <u>healthy</u> and <u>green</u>.

2) But the same plant grown in darkness would grow <u>tall and spindly</u> and its leaves would turn <u>yellow</u>.

Most Characteristics are Due to Genes AND the Environment

1) <u>Most characteristics</u> are controlled by a <u>mixture</u> of <u>genetic</u> and <u>environmental</u> factors.
2) E.g. <u>height</u> of sunflowers = genes + how much sunshine.

My mum's got no trousers — because I've got her jeans...

So, you are the way you are partly because of the genes you inherited from your folks. But you can't blame it <u>all</u> on your parents, since your <u>environment</u> then takes over and begins to shape you in all sorts of ways. In fact, it's often really tricky to decide which factor <u>has more effect</u>, your genes or the environment.

Genes and Chromosomes

It's <u>dead important</u> you get to grips with all the stuff on this page.

1) Most cells in your body have a <u>nucleus</u>.
2) The nucleus contains <u>chromosomes</u>.

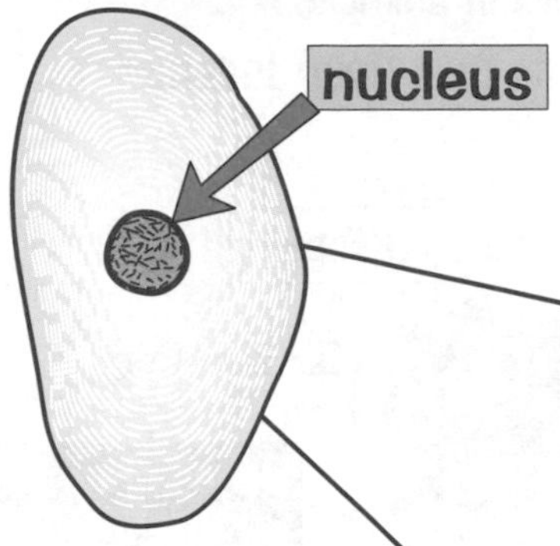

nucleus

3) The human cell nucleus contains <u>23 pairs of chromosomes</u>.
4) There are two No. 19 chromosomes, two No. 12s, two No. 3s, etc.

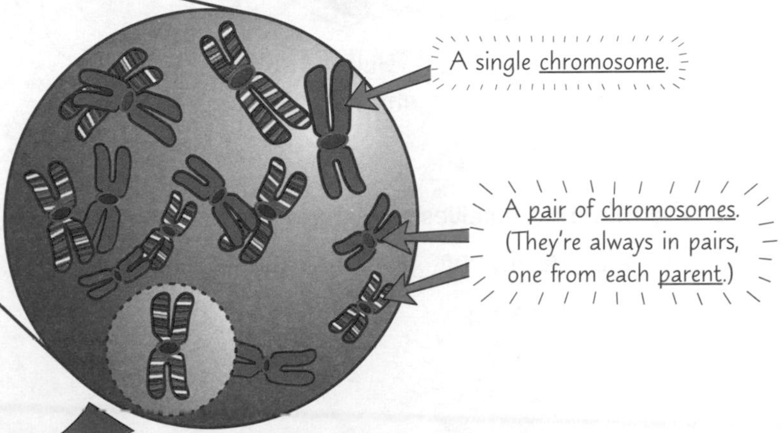

A single <u>chromosome</u>.

A <u>pair</u> of <u>chromosomes</u>. (They're always in pairs, one from each <u>parent</u>.)

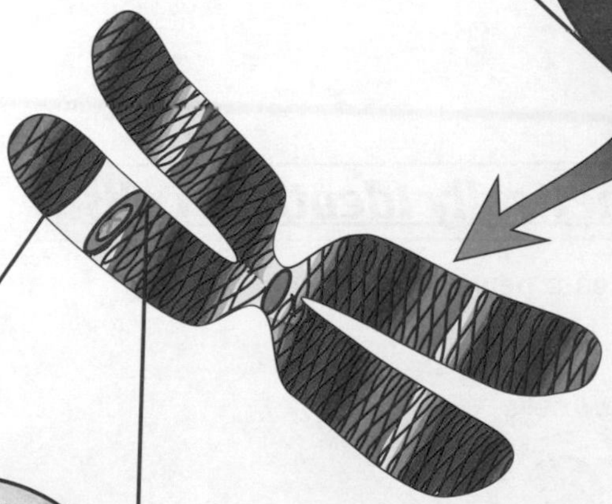

5) Chromosomes carry <u>genes</u>.
6) Different genes <u>control</u> the development of different <u>characteristics</u>, e.g. hair colour.

7) A <u>gene</u> is a <u>short length</u> of the chromosome but quite a long length of <u>DNA</u>.

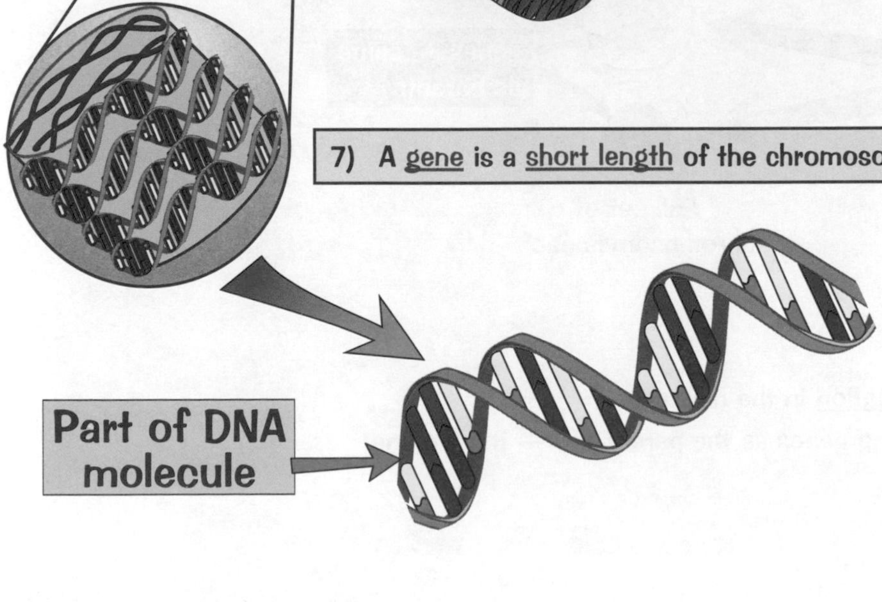

Part of DNA molecule

It's hard being a chromosome, there's so much to remember...

You definitely need to understand <u>everything</u> on this page or you'll find the rest of this topic hard. The best way to get these facts in your mind is to <u>cover</u> the page, <u>scribble</u> down the main points and <u>sketch</u> out the diagrams...

Reproduction

Ooo err, reproduction... Surely you knew it'd come up at some point. It can happen in two different ways...

Sexual Reproduction Produces Genetically Different Cells

1) Sexual reproduction is where genes from two organisms (a father and a mother) are mixed.
2) The mother and father produce gametes — e.g. egg and sperm cells in animals.
3) The egg (from the mother) and the sperm cell (from the father) then fuse (join) together.

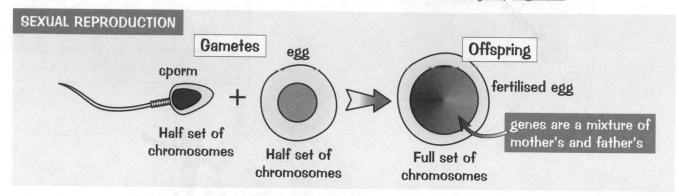

SEXUAL REPRODUCTION

Gametes

cporm — Half set of chromosomes

egg — Half set of chromosomes

Offspring — fertilised egg — Full set of chromosomes

genes are a mixture of mother's and father's

4) The offspring receives a mixture of chromosomes, so inherits features from both parents.
5) This mixture of genes produces variation in the offspring. Pretty cool, eh.

Asexual Reproduction Produces Genetically Identical Cells

1) Asexual reproduction is where one parent cell makes a new cell by dividing in two.

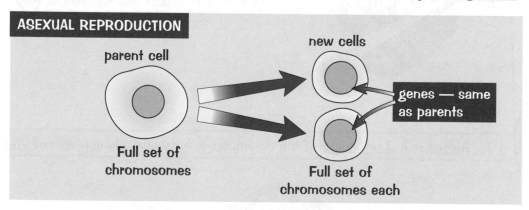

ASEXUAL REPRODUCTION

parent cell — Full set of chromosomes

new cells — Full set of chromosomes each

genes — same as parents

2) There's no fusion of gametes.
3) So there's no mixing of genes.
4) This means there's no genetic variation in the new cells.
5) Each new cell has exactly the same genes as the parent cell — it's a clone.

You need to reproduce these facts in the exam...

The main messages on this page are that: 1) sexual reproduction needs two parents, and it forms cells that are genetically different to the parents, so there's lots of genetic variation. And 2) asexual reproduction needs just one parent to make genetically identical cells (clones), so there's no genetic variation in the offspring.

Cloning

We can clone plants and animals in several <u>different ways</u>. But some of these ways could cause problems...

Plants Can Be Cloned from Cuttings and by Tissue Culture

1) Gardeners take <u>cuttings</u> from good parent plants and plant them to make <u>copies</u> with the <u>same genes</u> (<u>clones</u>).

2) Taking cuttings is <u>quick</u> and <u>cheap</u>.

3) <u>Tissue culture</u> is where you take <u>a few plant cells</u> and grow them into <u>new plants</u> — <u>clones</u> of the parent plant.

You Can Make Animal Clones Using Embryo Transplants

Farmers can produce <u>cloned offspring</u> from their best bull and cow — using <u>embryo transplants</u>.

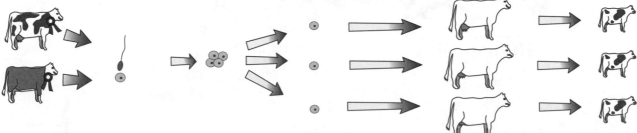

1) Prize <u>bull</u> and <u>cow</u> are <u>mated</u>.

2) An <u>embryo</u> develops.

3) The <u>embryo</u> is then <u>split</u> many times, <u>before</u> any cells become <u>specialised</u> (able to do a certain job).

4) The <u>embryos</u> are put into the wombs of (<u>implanted</u> into) lots of other cows.

5) The embryos are <u>clones</u>, so all the baby calves will have the <u>same genes</u>.

Adult Cell Cloning is Another Way to Make a Clone

1) <u>Adult cell cloning</u> involves taking an <u>unfertilised egg cell</u> and removing the nucleus.

2) The <u>nucleus</u> from an <u>adult body cell</u> (e.g. a skin cell) is put into the 'empty' egg cell.

3) An <u>electric shock</u> makes the egg cell <u>divide</u>.

4) When the embryo is a ball of cells, it's <u>implanted</u> into the womb of an <u>adult female</u>.

5) The embryo grows into a <u>clone</u> of the original adult body cell.

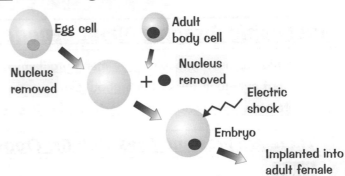

Egg cell

Adult body cell

Nucleus removed

Nucleus removed

Electric shock

Embryo

Implanted into adult female

There are Many Issues Surrounding Cloning

1) Cloning <u>quickly</u> gets you <u>lots of</u> "ideal" offspring.

2) <u>Studying</u> clones could also help us <u>understand</u> some <u>diseases</u>.

3) However cloned organisms all have the <u>same genes</u>, so if a disease appears they could all be <u>wiped out</u>.

4) It's possible that cloned animals might <u>not be as healthy</u> as normal ones.

Thank goodness they didn't do that with my little brother...

Remember the different types of cloning — cuttings, tissue culture, embryo transplants and adult cell cloning.

Genetic Engineering

Scientists can now <u>change</u> an organism's <u>genes</u> to alter its characteristics. This is a new science with exciting possibilities, but there might be <u>dangers</u> too...

Genetic Engineering Uses Enzymes to Cut and Paste Genes

1) A useful gene is "<u>cut</u>" from one organism's chromosome using <u>enzymes</u>.

2) <u>Enzymes</u> are then used to <u>cut</u> another organism's chromosome and then to <u>insert</u> the useful gene. For example:

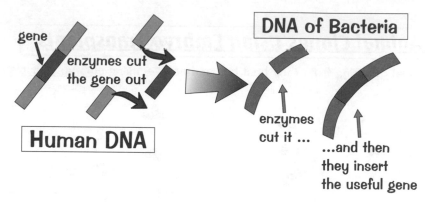

Genes can be Transferred into Animals and Plants

1) <u>Useful genes</u> can be transferred into <u>animals</u> and <u>plants</u> at the <u>very early stages</u> of their development.

2) This means they'll develop <u>useful characteristics</u>.

3) <u>Genetically modified</u> (<u>GM</u>) <u>crops</u> have had their genes modified (changed).
    E.g. to make them <u>resistant to viruses</u>, <u>insects</u> or <u>herbicides</u> (chemicals used to kill weeds).

But People Disagree About Genetic Engineering...

1) Genetic engineering could <u>solve</u> many <u>problems</u> e.g. treating <u>diseases</u>, more efficient <u>food production</u>.

2) But not everyone thinks it's a <u>good idea</u>.

3) There are <u>worries</u> about the <u>long-term effects</u> of genetic engineering.

There Are Pros and Cons With GM Crops

PROS

1) GM crops can <u>increase the yield</u> of a crop, making <u>more food</u>.

2) GM crops can include extra <u>nutrients</u> to <u>prevent deficiency diseases</u> (see page 13).

CONS

1) Growing GM crops could affect the <u>number of flowers and insects</u> that live by the crops.

2) Some people are worried that GM crops are not <u>safe to eat</u>.

If only there was a gene to make revision easier...

GM crops — a disaster in the making, or a brilliant invention? Make sure you know both sides of the debate.

Evolution

THEORY OF EVOLUTION: More than 3 billion years ago, life on Earth began as simple organisms from which all the more complex organisms evolved.

All Organisms are Related... even if Only Distantly

Looking at the similarities and differences between organisms means we can:

1) CLASSIFY them into groups
1) Plants make their own food.
2) Animals move about the place.
3) Microorganisms are different to plants and animals.

2) Understand how things are related (EVOLUTIONARY relationships).
1) Species with similar characteristics often have similar genes because they share a recent common ancestor.
2) This means they are closely related.
3) Evolutionary trees show common ancestors and relationships between organisms.
4) The more recent the common ancestor, the more closely related the two species.

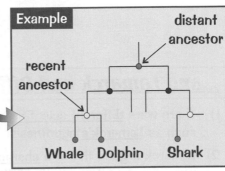

Whales and dolphins have a recent common ancestor — so they are closely related.

3) Understand how things interact (ECOLOGICAL relationships).

If we see organisms in the same environment with similar characteristics (e.g. dolphins and sharks) it suggests they might be in competition (e.g for the same food source).

Natural Selection Explains How Evolution Occurs

Charles Darwin came up with the idea of natural selection. It works like this...
1) Individuals within a species show variation because of the differences in their genes.
2) Individuals with characteristics that make them better adapted to the environment have a better chance of survival and so are more likely to breed successfully.
3) So the genes that control the useful characteristics are more likely to be passed on to the next generation.

Evolution can Occur Due To Mutations

1) A mutation is a change in an organism's DNA.
2) Most mutations have no effect, but sometimes they can be helpful by producing a useful characteristic.
3) This characteristic may give the organism a better chance of surviving and reproducing.
4) If so, the helpful mutation is more likely to be passed on to future generations by natural selection.
5) Over time, the helpful mutation will become more common in a population.
6) For example, some species of bacteria have become resistant to antibiotics due to a mutation (see p.17).

"Natural selection" — sounds like vegan chocolates...
Natural selection's all about organisms with the best features surviving. It doesn't happen overnight though.

More About Evolution

Nowadays there's lots of evidence for evolution by natural selection that Charlie Darwin didn't have at the time.

Not Everyone Agreed with Darwin...

Darwin's idea wasn't accepted at the time — for various reasons...

1) It went against common religious beliefs that life on Earth was made by a "Creator" (God).

2) Darwin couldn't explain how new characteristics appeared or were passed on to offspring.

3) There wasn't enough evidence yet to convince many scientists.

...and Lamarck had Different Ideas

1) There were different scientific hypotheses about evolution around at the same time, such as Lamarck's hypothesis.

2) Lamarck argued that if a characteristic was used a lot by an organism then it would become more developed during its lifetime.

3) He believed these developed characteristics would be passed on to the next generation.

Scientists can Develop Different Hypotheses from Similar Observations

1) Often scientists come up with different hypotheses to explain similar observations.

2) Scientists might develop different hypotheses because they have different beliefs, or they have been influenced by different people, or they just think differently.

3) The only way to find out whose hypothesis is right is to find evidence to support or disprove each one.

4) For example, Lamarck and Darwin both had different hypotheses to explain how evolution happens:

   1) Lamarck's theory was eventually rejected because experiments didn't support his hypothesis.
   2) The discovery of genetics supported Darwin's idea.
   3) Genes provided an explanation of how organisms born with helpful characteristics can pass them on.

5) There's so much evidence for Darwin's idea that it's now an accepted hypothesis (a theory).

There's more about how science works on page 2.

Did you know that exams evolved from medieval torture...

This is a good example of how scientific hypotheses come about — someone observes something and then tries to explain it. Their hypothesis will then be tested by other scientists — if their evidence supports the hypothesis, more people agree with it. If not, it's rejected. Darwin's theory hasn't been rejected yet.

Revision Summary for Biology 1b

There's a lot to remember from this section and not everyone agrees about some of the topics, like cloning and genetic engineering. You need to know all sides of the story, as well as all the facts. So, here are some questions to help you figure out what you know. If you get any wrong, go back and learn the stuff.

1) Name four ways in which a desert animal may be adapted to its environment.

2) State three ways that plants and animals might be adapted to scare away predators.

3) Name three things that: a) plants compete for, b) animals compete for.

4) Give two examples of non-living factors that can cause environmental changes.

5) What does lots of lichen growing somewhere indicate?

6) Name an organism that can be used as an indicator of water pollution.

7) What does each bar on a pyramid of biomass show?

8) Give two ways that energy is lost from a food chain.

9) Give one way that carbon dioxide from the air enters a food chain.

10) Give three ways that carbon compounds in a food chain become carbon dioxide in the air again.

11) What is environmental variation?

12) How many pairs of chromosomes do humans have in each body cell?

13) The table below compares sexual and asexual reproduction.
    Complete the table by ticking each statement that is true for sexual or asexual reproduction.

	Sexual reproduction	Asexual reproduction
Reproduction involves two parents.		
Offspring are clones of the parent.		
There is variation in the offspring.		
There is no fusion of gametes.		

14) How would you make a plant clone using tissue culture?

15) Give two pros of GM crops.

16) Give two cons of GM crops.

17) Give the three main steps in Darwin's theory of natural selection.

18) Give two reasons why Darwin's idea wasn't accepted by everyone when he suggested it.

Atoms and Elements

Atoms are the building blocks of <u>everything</u> — and they're <u>really, really tiny</u>.

Atoms have a Small Nucleus Surrounded by Electrons

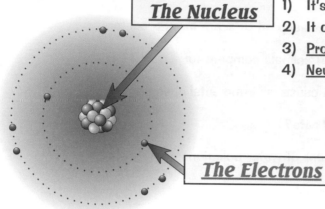

The Nucleus
1) It's in the <u>middle</u> of the atom.
2) It contains <u>protons</u> and <u>neutrons</u>.
3) <u>Protons</u> are <u>positively (+) charged</u>.
4) <u>Neutrons</u> have <u>no charge</u> (they're neutral).

The Electrons
1) Move <u>around</u> the nucleus.
2) They're <u>negatively (−) charged</u>.
3) They occupy <u>shells</u> around the nucleus.

Number of Protons Equals Number of Electrons

1) Atoms have <u>no charge</u> overall. They're neutral.
2) The <u>charge</u> on the electrons is the <u>same</u> size as the charge on the <u>protons</u> — but <u>opposite</u>.
3) This means the <u>number</u> of <u>protons</u> always equals the <u>number</u> of <u>electrons</u> in an <u>atom</u>.
4) If some electrons are <u>added or removed</u>, the atom becomes <u>charged</u> and is then an <u>ion</u>.

Elements Consist of One Type of Atom Only

1) Atoms can have different numbers of protons, neutrons and electrons.
   It's the number of <u>protons</u> in the nucleus that decides what <u>type</u> of atom it is.
2) For example, an atom with <u>one proton</u> in its nucleus is <u>hydrogen</u>. An atom with <u>two protons</u> is <u>helium</u>.
3) If a substance only contains <u>one type</u> of atom it's called an <u>element</u>.
4) There are about <u>100 different elements</u> — quite a lot of everyday substances are elements:

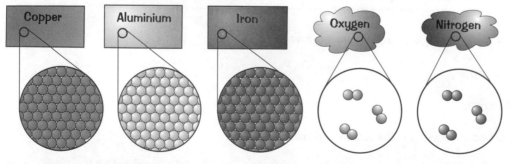

So <u>all the atoms</u> of a particular <u>element</u> (e.g. nitrogen) have the <u>same number</u> of protons...

...and <u>different elements</u> have atoms with <u>different numbers</u> of protons.

Number of protons = number of electrons...

You need to <u>know these basic facts</u> — then you'll have a better chance of understanding the rest of Chemistry.

The Periodic Table

The periodic table is a chemist's best friend — start getting to know it now... seriously...

Atoms Can be Represented by Symbols

Atoms of each element are given a <u>one or two letter symbol</u>. E.g.

| C = carbon | O = oxygen | Mg = magnesium | Na = sodium | Fe = iron |

The Periodic Table Puts Elements <u>with Similar Properties Together</u>

1) Elements with <u>similar properties</u> are put into <u>columns</u>.
   These <u>vertical columns</u> are called <u>groups</u>.

2) All of the elements in a <u>group</u> have the <u>same number</u> of <u>electrons</u> in their <u>outer shell</u>.

3) If you know the <u>properties</u> of <u>one element</u>, you can <u>predict</u> properties of <u>other elements</u> in that group.
   For example, the <u>Group 1</u> elements include lithium (Li), sodium (Na) and potassium (K).
   They're all <u>metals</u> and they <u>react the same way</u> with water and oxygen.

4) The elements in the final column (<u>Group 0</u>) are the <u>noble gases</u>.

5) Noble gases all have <u>eight electrons</u> in their <u>outer shell</u>, apart from helium (which has two).
   This means that they're <u>unreactive</u>.

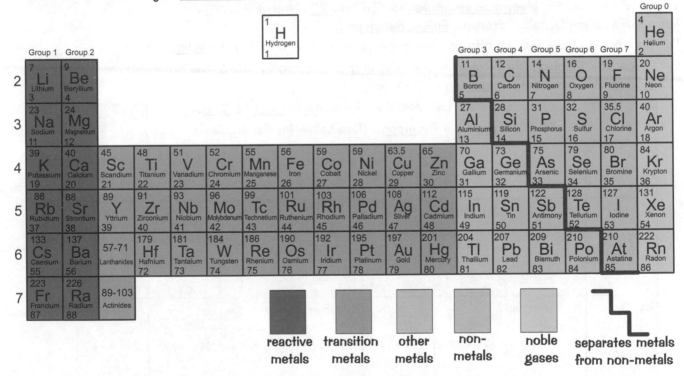

6) There are a lot of numbers in the periodic table. Here's what they mean:

This is the <u>mass number</u>. It's the total number of protons and neutrons.

This is the <u>atomic number</u>. It's the number of protons. And it's the same as the <u>number of electrons</u>.

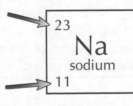

The number of neutrons in an atom is the atomic number minus (take away) the mass number.

<u>I'm in a chemistry band — I play the symbols...</u>

You <u>don't</u> need to know the properties of each group of the periodic table. But if you're told, for example, that helium (Group 0) is <u>unreactive</u>, it's a fair guess that neon, argon, krypton, xenon and radon <u>are too</u>.

Electron Shells

The fact that electrons hang out in "shells" around the nucleus is what causes the whole of chemistry.

Electron Shell Rules:

1) Electrons always occupy <u>shells</u> (sometimes called <u>energy levels</u>).

2) The <u>inner shells</u> are <u>always filled first</u> — these are the ones closest to the nucleus.

3) Only <u>a certain number</u> of electrons are allowed in each shell:
   1st shell: 2   2nd shell: 8   3rd shell: 8

4) Atoms are much <u>happier</u> when they have <u>full</u> electron shells — like the <u>noble gases</u> in Group 0.

5) In most atoms the <u>outer shell</u> is <u>not full</u> and this makes the atom want to <u>react</u> to fill it.

3rd shell still filling

Follow the Rules to Work Out Electronic Structures

You need to know the <u>electronic structures</u> for the first <u>20</u> elements.
For a quick example, take nitrogen. <u>Follow the steps...</u>

1) The periodic table tells us nitrogen has <u>seven</u> protons... so it must have <u>seven</u> electrons.

2) Follow the 'Electron Shell Rules' above. The <u>first</u> shell can only take 2 electrons and the <u>second</u> shell can take a <u>maximum</u> of 8 electrons.

3) So the electronic structure for nitrogen <u>must</u> be 2, 5.

4) Now <u>you</u> try it for <u>argon</u>. (See below for the answer.)

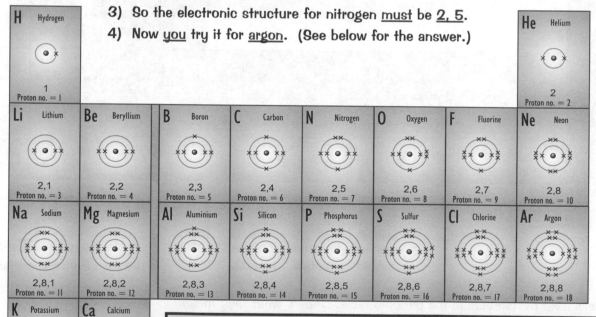

Answer... To calculate the electronic structure of argon, <u>follow the rules</u>. It's got 18 protons, so it <u>must</u> have 18 electrons. The first shell must have <u>2</u> electrons, the second shell must have <u>8</u>, and so the third shell must have <u>8</u> as well. It's as easy as <u>2, 8, 8</u>.

One little duck and two fat ladies — 2, 8, 8...

You need to know enough about electron shells to draw out that <u>whole diagram</u> at the bottom of the page without looking at it. The best thing to do is to just <u>learn the pattern</u> — don't learn each element separately.

Compounds and Chemical Reactions

Elements don't just stay solo — they link up with other elements to make <u>compounds</u>.

Atoms Join Together to Make Compounds

1) When <u>different elements react</u>, atoms join together with other atoms to form <u>compounds</u>. In a compound the atoms are joined by <u>chemical bonds</u>.

2) <u>Making bonds</u> involves atoms giving away, taking or sharing <u>electrons</u>.

3) A compound which is formed from a <u>metal</u> and a <u>non-metal</u> is made up of <u>ions</u>. This is what happens when the compound forms:

- The <u>metal</u> atoms <u>lose</u> electrons to form <u>positive ions</u>.
- The non-metal atoms <u>gain</u> electrons to form <u>negative ions</u>.
- The <u>opposite charges</u> (positive and negative) of the ions mean that they're strongly <u>attracted</u> to each other.
- This is called <u>IONIC</u> bonding.

E.g. sodium chloride (NaCl) is a compound formed from a metal (sodium) and a non-metal (chlorine).

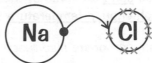

The sodium atom <u>loses</u> an electron.
The chlorine atom <u>gains</u> an electron.

4) A compound formed from <u>non-metals</u> is made up of <u>molecules</u>. This is what happens when the compound forms:

- Each atom <u>shares</u> an <u>electron</u> with another atom — this is called a <u>COVALENT</u> bond.
- Each atom has to make enough covalent bonds to <u>fill up</u> its <u>outer shell</u>.

E.g. hydrochloric acid (HCl) is a compound formed from two non-metals (hydrogen and chlorine).

A hydrogen atom bonds with a chlorine atom by <u>sharing</u> an electron with it.

Atoms Aren't Lost or Made in Chemical Reactions

1) A reaction can be shown by a <u>word equation</u> or a <u>symbol equation</u>. The word equation shows the <u>names</u> of the chemicals reacting. The symbol equation uses the <u>one or two letter symbols</u> (see page 45). For example:

Word equation:	magnesium + oxygen → magnesium oxide
Symbol equation:	$2Mg + O_2 \rightarrow 2MgO$
The symbol equation shows the number of atoms:	

2) You still have the <u>same atoms</u> at the <u>end</u> of a chemical reaction as you had at the <u>start</u>. No <u>atoms</u> are lost or made. They're just <u>arranged</u> in different ways.

3) The mass of the <u>reactants</u> (the substances you start with) <u>equals</u> the mass of the <u>products</u> (what you end up with). So, if you react <u>6 g of magnesium</u> with <u>4 g of oxygen</u>, you'd end up with <u>10 g of magnesium oxide</u>.

Not learning this stuff will only compound your problems...

Make sure you understand <u>what compounds are</u> and how they form. It's also a good idea to <u>practise</u> writing <u>word equations</u> for reactions. This stuff is a bit tricky so take it <u>slowly</u> and go through it one step at a time.

Using Limestone

Limestone's <u>quarried</u> (dug up) out of the ground and then used as a <u>building material</u>...

Limestone is Mainly Calcium Carbonate

1) Limestone is mainly <u>calcium carbonate</u> — $CaCO_3$.

2) When it's heated it <u>thermally decomposes</u> (breaks down in the heat) to make <u>calcium oxide</u> and <u>carbon dioxide</u>.

$$\text{calcium carbonate} \rightarrow \text{calcium oxide} + \text{carbon dioxide}$$

- When <u>magnesium</u>, <u>copper</u>, <u>zinc</u> and <u>sodium carbonates</u> are heated, they decompose in the <u>same way</u>. E.g. magnesium carbonate › magnesium oxide + carbon dioxide

- You <u>can't</u> do some of these reactions in class — a <u>Bunsen burner</u> can't reach a <u>high enough temperature</u> to thermally decompose some carbonates of <u>Group 1 metals</u>.

3) Calcium carbonate also reacts with <u>acid</u> to make a <u>calcium salt</u>, <u>carbon dioxide</u> and <u>water</u>.

$$\text{calcium carbonate} + \text{sulfuric acid} \rightarrow \text{calcium sulfate} + \text{carbon dioxide} + \text{water}$$

- The type of <u>salt</u> produced <u>depends</u> on the type of <u>acid</u>. For example, a reaction with <u>hydrochloric</u> acid would make a <u>chloride</u> (e.g. $CaCl_2$).

- Other carbonates that react with acids are <u>magnesium</u>, <u>copper</u>, <u>zinc</u> and <u>sodium</u>.

Calcium Oxide Reacts with Water to Produce Calcium Hydroxide

1) When you <u>add water</u> to calcium oxide you get <u>calcium hydroxide</u>.

$$\text{calcium oxide} + \text{water} \rightarrow \text{calcium hydroxide}$$

2) Calcium hydroxide is an <u>alkali</u> which can be used to neutralise <u>acidic soil</u> in fields.

3) When calcium hydroxide is mixed with water it makes a <u>solution</u> called <u>limewater</u>. Limewater can be used as a <u>test</u> for <u>carbon dioxide</u>. If you bubble <u>gas</u> through it, the solution will turn <u>cloudy</u> if the gas is <u>carbon dioxide</u>. This is the reaction:

$$\text{calcium hydroxide} + \text{carbon dioxide} \rightarrow \text{calcium carbonate} + \text{water}$$

Limestone is Used to Make Other Useful Things Too

1) Limestone can be <u>heated</u> with <u>clay</u> to make <u>cement</u>.

2) Cement can be mixed with <u>sand</u> and <u>water</u> to make <u>mortar</u>. <u>Mortar</u> is the stuff you stick <u>bricks</u> together with.

3) Or you can mix cement with <u>sand</u> and <u>aggregate</u> (<u>water</u> and <u>gravel</u>) to make <u>concrete</u>.

Limestone — also in lemon and apple flavour...

Wow. It sounds like you can build <u>pretty much anything</u> with limestone, possibly apart from a bouncy castle. Loads of <u>famous buildings</u> are made out of limestone so it's pretty important stuff.

Using Limestone

Limestone isn't perfect — digging it out of the ground and making stuff from it causes quite a few <u>problems</u>.

Quarrying Limestone Makes a Right Mess of the Landscape

Digging limestone out of the ground can cause environmental problems.

1) For a start, it makes <u>huge ugly holes</u> which change the landscape for ever.

2) <u>Quarrying</u> means blasting rocks apart with explosives. This makes lots of <u>noise</u> and <u>dust</u>.

3) Quarrying <u>destroys the homes</u> of animals and birds.

4) The limestone needs to be <u>transported away</u> from the quarry — usually in lorries. This causes more noise and pollution.

5) Waste materials produce unsightly <u>tips</u>.

Making Stuff from Limestone Causes Pollution Too

1) <u>Cement factories</u> make a lot of <u>dust</u>. This can cause <u>breathing problems</u> for some people.

2) <u>Energy</u> is needed to produce cement. The energy is likely to come from burning <u>fossil fuels</u>, which causes pollution.

See page 59 for more on pollution caused by burning fossil fuels.

But on the Plus Side...

1) Limestone provides things that people want — like <u>houses</u> and <u>roads</u>. Chemicals used in making <u>dyes</u>, <u>paints</u> and <u>medicines</u> also come from limestone.

2) Limestone products are used to <u>neutralise acidic soil</u>, <u>lakes</u> and <u>rivers</u>.

3) Limestone is also used in power station chimneys to <u>neutralise sulfur dioxide</u>, which is a cause of acid rain.

4) The quarry provides <u>jobs</u> for people and brings more money into the <u>local economy</u>.

Limestone Products Have Advantages and Disadvantages

Limestone and concrete (made from cement) are used as <u>building materials</u>. In some cases they're <u>perfect</u> for the job, but in other cases they aren't so great.

1) Limestone is found in <u>large amounts</u> in the UK and is <u>cheaper</u> than granite or marble. It's also a fairly easy rock to <u>cut</u>.

2) Some limestone is more <u>hard-wearing</u> than marble, but it still looks <u>nice</u>.

3) However, limestone can be <u>damaged</u> by <u>acid rain</u> (see page 59).

4) Concrete can be poured into <u>moulds</u> to make blocks or panels that can be joined together. It's a <u>very quick and cheap</u> way of making buildings, <u>and it shows</u> — concrete is <u>ugly</u>.

5) Limestone, concrete and cement <u>don't rot</u> when they get wet like wood does. They can't be eaten by <u>insects</u> or <u>rodents</u> either. And to top it off, they <u>can't</u> be set on <u>fire</u>.

6) Concrete <u>doesn't corrode</u> (break down or rust) like lots of metals do. It can crack though. <u>Steel bars</u> can be used to make it stronger.

Tough revision here — this stuff's rock hard...

There's a <u>downside</u> to everything, including using limestone — huge quarries definitely <u>spoil the countryside</u>. But you have to find a <u>balance</u> between looking after the environment, making money and building things.

Getting Metals from Rocks

A few <u>unreactive metals</u> like <u>gold</u> are found in the Earth as the <u>metal itself</u>. But most metals are found as <u>compounds</u> in rocks. Getting the pure metal is called <u>extraction</u>.

Ores Contain Enough Metal to Make Extraction Worthwhile

1) A <u>metal ore</u> is a <u>rock</u> which contains <u>enough metal</u> to make it <u>worthwhile</u> extracting the metal from it. In many cases the ore is an <u>oxide</u> of the metal.

2) <u>Most metals</u> need to be extracted from their ores using a <u>chemical reaction</u>.

3) How much <u>money</u> you can make from metal extraction can <u>change</u> over <u>time</u>. For example:
   - If the market <u>price</u> of a metal <u>drops</u> a lot, it <u>might not</u> be worth extracting it.
   - If the <u>price increases</u> a lot then it <u>might be worth</u> extracting <u>more</u> of it.

Metals Are Extracted From their Ores Chemically

1) A metal can be extracted from its ore by <u>reduction</u> (see below) or by <u>electrolysis</u> (splitting with electricity, see page 51).

2) Some ores may have to be <u>concentrated</u> before the metal is extracted — this just involves getting rid of the <u>unwanted rocky material</u>.

3) <u>Electrolysis</u> can also be used to <u>purify</u> the extracted metal (see page 51).

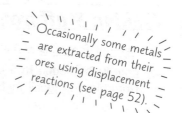
Occasionally some metals are extracted from their ores using displacement reactions (see page 52).

Some Metals can be Extracted by Reduction with Carbon

1) A metal can be <u>extracted</u> from its ore by <u>reduction</u> using <u>carbon</u>.

2) When an ore is reduced, <u>oxygen is removed</u> from it. E.g. the oxygen is removed from iron oxide to extract the iron.

| iron oxide | + | carbon | → | iron | + | carbon dioxide |

3) Metals can be put in a <u>list</u> of <u>how reactive</u> they are. This is known as the <u>reactivity series</u>.

4) The position of the metal in the <u>reactivity series</u> shows whether it can be extracted by <u>reduction</u> with carbon.

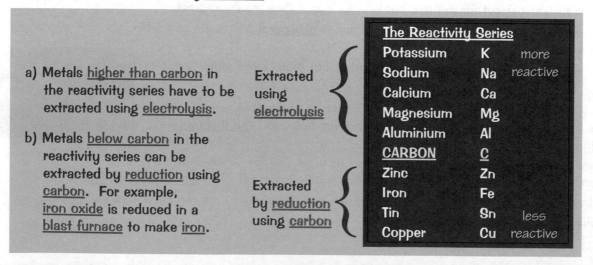

a) Metals <u>higher than carbon</u> in the reactivity series have to be extracted using <u>electrolysis</u>.

b) Metals <u>below carbon</u> in the reactivity series can be extracted by <u>reduction</u> using <u>carbon</u>. For example, <u>iron oxide</u> is reduced in a <u>blast furnace</u> to make <u>iron</u>.

Extracted using electrolysis

Extracted by reduction using carbon

The Reactivity Series

Potassium	K	more reactive
Sodium	Na	
Calcium	Ca	
Magnesium	Mg	
Aluminium	Al	
<u>CARBON</u>	<u>C</u>	
Zinc	Zn	
Iron	Fe	
Tin	Sn	less reactive
Copper	Cu	

Learn how metals are extracted — ore else...

Extracting metals isn't cheap. If there's a choice of extraction methods, a company always picks the <u>cheapest</u>, unless there's a good reason not to (e.g. to increase purity). They're <u>not</u> extracting it for fun.

Getting Metals from Rocks

You may think you know all you could ever need to know about how to get metals from rocks, but no — there's <u>more</u> of it. Think of each of the facts on this page as a little <u>gold nugget</u>. Or, er, a copper one.

Some Metals have to be Extracted by Electrolysis

1) Metals that are <u>more reactive</u> than carbon (see previous page) have to be extracted using <u>electrolysis</u>.
2) Electrolysis is the <u>breaking down</u> of a substance using <u>electricity</u>.
3) It requires a <u>liquid</u> to <u>conduct</u> the <u>electricity</u>.
4) The liquid is often a <u>metal salt solution</u> or a <u>molten metal oxide</u>.

> A metal that has to be extracted by electrolysis is <u>aluminium</u>.
> - A <u>high temperature</u> is needed to <u>melt</u> aluminium oxide so that <u>aluminium</u> can be extracted.
> - This uses a lot of <u>energy</u>, which makes it an <u>expensive</u> process.

Copper is Purified by Electrolysis

1) Copper can be easily extracted by <u>reduction with carbon</u> (see previous page). The ore is <u>heated</u> in a <u>furnace</u> (a kind of oven) — this is called <u>smelting</u>.
2) However, the copper produced this way is <u>impure</u> — and impure copper <u>doesn't</u> conduct electricity very well. This <u>isn't</u> very <u>useful</u> because a lot of copper is used to make <u>electrical wiring</u>.
3) So <u>electrolysis</u> is also used to <u>purify</u> it, even though it's quite <u>expensive</u>.
4) This produces <u>very pure</u> copper, which is a <u>much better conductor</u>.

> Here's how electrolysis can be used to get pure <u>copper</u>.
> 1) A <u>copper salt solution</u> is used to conduct the electricity.
> 2) Copper atoms from the <u>positive electrode</u> turn into Cu^{2+} ions. They go into the copper salt solution.
> 3) The Cu^{2+} ions move towards the <u>negative electrode</u>.
> 4) At the negative electrode the ions turn into <u>copper atoms</u> — making pure copper metal.

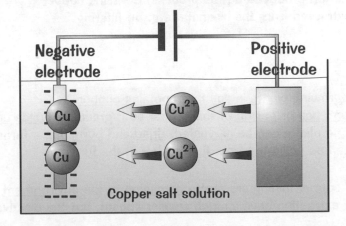

The negative electrode is a piece of pure copper. More pure copper adds to it.

Negative electrode

Positive electrode

The positive electrode is a lump of impure copper.

Copper salt solution

Someone stolen your metal? — call a copper...

The skin of the <u>Statue of Liberty</u> is made of copper — about 80 tonnes of it in fact. Its surface reacts with gases in the air to form <u>copper carbonate</u> — which is why it's that pretty shade of <u>green</u>.

Getting Metals from Rocks

Just to top it off, you need to know even more about copper extraction... sigh, it's a hard life.

You Can Extract Copper From a Solution Using a Displacement Reaction

1) If you put a reactive metal into a solution of a metal compound dissolved in water, the reactive metal will replace the less reactive metal in the compound.

2) This is because the more reactive metal bonds more strongly to the non-metal bit of the compound and pushes out the less reactive metal.

3) For example, scrap iron can be used to displace (push out) copper from solution. If some iron is put in a solution of copper sulfate, the more reactive iron will "kick out" the less reactive copper from the solution. You end up with iron sulfate solution and copper metal.

$$\text{copper sulfate} + \text{iron} \rightarrow \text{iron sulfate} + \text{copper}$$

Copper-rich Ores are in Short Supply

1) The supply of copper-rich ores is limited, so it's important to recycle as much copper as possible.

2) The demand for copper is growing and this may lead to shortages in the future.

3) Scientists are looking into new ways of extracting copper from low-grade ores. These are ores that only contain small amounts of copper.

4) They're also looking at ways to extract extra copper from the waste that's currently produced during extraction.

5) Examples of new methods used to extract copper are bioleaching and phytomining:

Bioleaching

This uses bacteria to separate copper from copper sulfide. The leachate (the solution produced by the process) contains copper. The copper can be extracted from the leachate, e.g. by filtering.

Phytomining

This involves growing plants in soil that contains copper. The plants can't use or get rid of the copper so it gradually builds up in the leaves. The plants can be harvested, dried and burned in a furnace. The copper can be collected from the ash left in the furnace.

Phyto just means plant — so phytomining = plant mining.

6) Traditional methods of copper mining are pretty damaging to the environment (see next page). These new methods of extraction have a much smaller impact, but the disadvantage is that they're slow.

Personally, I'd rather be pound rich than copper rich...

Pure copper is expensive but useful stuff. Just think where we'd be without good quality copper wire to conduct electricity. The fact that copper-rich ore supplies are getting low means that scientists have to come up with new methods to extract it. It also means that you have to learn all about it. Sorry about that.

Impacts of Extracting Metals

Metals are very useful. Just imagine if all knives and forks were made of plastic instead — they'd be snapping all over the place at dinner time. However, metal extraction uses a lot of <u>energy</u> and is <u>bad</u> for the <u>environment</u>. And that's where recycling comes in handy.

Metal Extraction can be Bad for the Environment

1) People have to balance the <u>social</u>, <u>economic</u> and <u>environmental</u> effects of mining the ores.

2) Most of the issues are exactly the same as those to do with quarrying limestone on page 49.

- So mining metal ores is <u>good</u> because it means that <u>useful products</u> can be made.
- It also provides local people with <u>jobs</u> and brings <u>money</u> into the area.

But...
- Mining ores is <u>bad for the environment</u> as it causes noise, damage to the landscape and loss of habitats.
- Deep mine shafts can also be <u>dangerous</u> for a long time after the mine has been abandoned.

Recycling Metals is Important

1) Mining and extracting metals takes lots of <u>energy</u>. Most of that energy comes from burning <u>fossil fuels</u>.

2) Fossil fuels are <u>running out</u> so it's important to <u>use less</u> of them. Also, burning fossil fuels is causing <u>acid rain</u>, <u>global dimming</u> and <u>climate change</u> (see pages 59 and 60).

3) Recycling metals uses <u>much less</u> energy than mining and extracting new metal.

4) Energy doesn't come cheap, so recycling <u>saves money</u> too.

5) Also, there's a <u>fixed amount</u> of each <u>metal</u> in the Earth. Recycling means the metals are less likely to run out.

6) Recycling metal cuts down on the amount of rubbish that gets sent to <u>landfill</u>. Landfill takes up space and <u>pollutes</u> the surroundings.

Recycling — good for metals, bad for jokes...

Recycling metals saves <u>natural resources</u> and <u>money</u> and reduces <u>environmental problems</u>. It's great. There's no limit to the number of times metals like aluminium, copper and steel can be recycled. So your humble little drink can may one day form part of a powerful robot who takes over the galaxy.

Properties of Metals

All metals have some things in common. However, they're not all exactly the same.

Metals are Strong and Bendy and They're Great Conductors

1) Most of the elements are metals — so they cover most of the periodic table. Only the elements on the far right are non-metals.

2) The metals in the centre block of the periodic table are called transition metals.

3) All metals have some fairly similar basic properties:
   - Metals are strong (hard to break), but they can be bent or hammered into different shapes.
   - They're great at conducting heat and electricity.

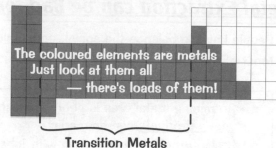

The coloured elements are metals
Just look at them all
— there's loads of them!

Transition Metals

4) This means metals have loads of everyday uses:
   - They're strong and can be bent so they are good for making into things like bridges and car bodies.
   - They're ideal if you're making something that heat needs to travel through, e.g. a saucepan base.
   - And they conduct electricity so they're great for making things like electrical wires.

A Metal's Exact Properties Decide How It's Best Used

1) The properties above are typical properties of metals. Not all metals are the same though:

Copper is a good conductor of electricity. It's hard and strong but can be bent. It also doesn't react with water.

Aluminium is corrosion-resistant (it doesn't break down easily). It also has a low density so it's light. Pure aluminium isn't very strong, but it forms hard, strong alloys (see page 55).

Titanium is another low density metal. It's very strong. It is also corrosion-resistant.

2) These metals have different uses because of their properties. For example:
   - Copper is great for plumbing. It can be bent to make pipes and tanks, and it doesn't react with water. Because it conducts electricity it's also great for making electrical wires.
   - Aluminium is used to make aeroplanes. It's strong and can be bent into shape. It's also light.
   - Titanium is used by doctors to make replacement hips for people. It won't corrode when it comes in contact with water. It's also light and not too bendy.

Metals are Good — but Not Perfect

1) Metals are very useful structural materials — they're used to make things like buildings.

2) However, some corrode when exposed to air and water, so they need to be protected. This can be done in lots of ways, e.g. by painting. If metals corrode, they lose their strength and hardness.

3) Metals can get 'tired' when they're under stress for a long time. This causes the metal to break.

Metals are great — if only they could take exams for you...

So, all metals conduct electricity and heat and can be bent into shape. But lots of them have special properties too. You have to decide what properties you need and use the metal with those properties.

Alloys

Pure metals often aren't quite right for certain jobs — and that's where alloys come in useful.

Impure Iron Tends to Break Easily

1) 'Iron' straight from the blast furnace is only 96% iron. The other 4% is impurities such as carbon.

2) This impure iron is used as cast iron. It's handy for making railings (e.g. in parks).

3) It doesn't have many other uses because it's brittle (easy to break). So all the impurities are removed from most of the blast furnace iron.

Most Iron is Converted into Steel — an Alloy

1) An alloy is a mixture of two or more metals, or a mixture of a metal and a non-metal.

2) Most pure iron is changed into alloys called steels.

3) Steels are formed by adding small amounts of carbon and sometimes other metals to the iron.

TYPE OF STEEL	PROPERTIES	USES
Low carbon steel (0.1% carbon)	easily shaped	car bodies
High carbon steel (1.5% carbon)	very hard, inflexible	blades for cutting tools, bridges
Stainless steel (chromium added, and sometimes nickel)	corrosion-resistant	cutlery, containers for corrosive substances

Alloys are Harder Than Pure Metals

1) Alloys are useful because they are harder than pure metals such as iron and gold.

2) Many metals in use today are actually alloys. E.g.:

CUPRONICKEL = COPPER + NICKEL — This is hard and corrosion resistant. It's used to make "silver" coins.

GOLD ALLOYS ARE USED TO MAKE JEWELLERY — Pure gold is too soft. Metals such as copper, silver, and nickel are used to harden the "gold".

ALUMINIUM ALLOYS ARE USED TO MAKE AIRCRAFT — Aluminium has a low density, but it's alloyed with small amounts of other metals to make it stronger.

3) Because we understand about the properties of metals we can design alloys for specific uses.

A brass band — harder than Iron Maiden...

The Eiffel Tower is made of iron — but the problem with iron is, it goes rusty if air and water get to it. So the Eiffel Tower has to be painted every seven years to make sure that it doesn't rust. This is quite a job and takes an entire year for a team of 25 painters. Too bad they didn't use stainless steel.

Fractional Distillation of Crude Oil

Crude oil is formed over millions of years from the buried remains of plants and animals — it's a fossil fuel.

Crude Oil is a Mixture of Hydrocarbons

1) A mixture consists of two (or more) elements or compounds that aren't chemically bonded to each other.

2) Crude oil is a mixture of many different compounds. Most of the compounds are hydrocarbon molecules.

3) Hydrocarbons are made of just carbon and hydrogen atoms.

4) There are no chemical bonds between the different parts of a mixture. This means that the different hydrocarbon molecules in crude oil aren't chemically bonded to one another.

5) This means that they all keep their original properties, such as their condensing points.

6) The parts of a mixture can be separated out by physical methods, e.g. crude oil can be split up into its separate parts (called fractions) by fractional distillation (see below).

7) Each fraction contains molecules with a similar number of carbon atoms to each other (see below).

Crude Oil is Split into Separate Groups of Hydrocarbons

1) The fractionating column works continuously (non-stop).

2) Heated crude oil is piped in at the bottom.

3) The oil evaporates (it forms a gas) and rises up the column.

4) The various fractions are constantly collected at the different levels where they condense (change from gas to liquid).

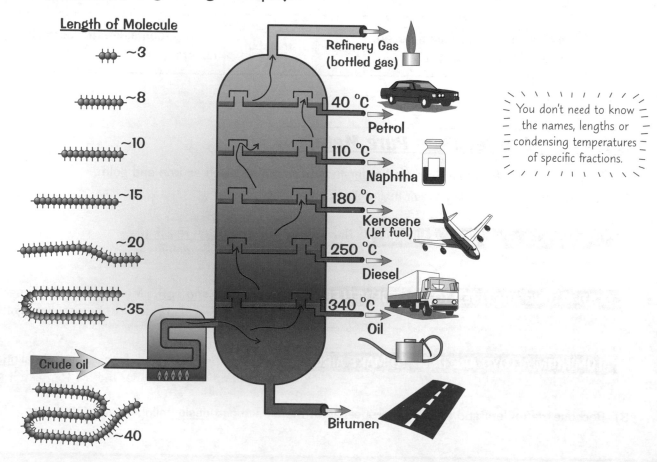

Length of Molecule

~3 — Refinery Gas (bottled gas)

~8 — 40 °C — Petrol

~10 — 110 °C — Naphtha

~15 — 180 °C — Kerosene (Jet fuel)

~20 — 250 °C — Diesel

~35 — 340 °C — Oil

Crude oil

~40 — Bitumen

You don't need to know the names, lengths or condensing temperatures of specific fractions.

Crude oil — it's always cracking dirty jokes...

When we burn crude oil fractions, e.g. petrol, kerosene or diesel oil, we're burning up non-renewable fuels. If we use it all, we're going to have to wait a long time to get any more (see page 58).

Properties and Uses of Crude Oil

The <u>different fractions</u> of crude oil have <u>different properties</u>, and it's all down to their <u>structure</u>. You need to know the <u>basic structure</u> and a few <u>trends</u>.

Crude Oil is Mostly Alkanes

1) All the fractions of crude oil are hydrocarbons called <u>alkanes</u>.
2) Alkanes are made up of <u>chains of carbon atoms</u> surrounded by <u>hydrogen atoms</u>.
3) Different alkanes have chains of different <u>lengths</u>.
4) The first four alkanes are <u>methane</u>, <u>ethane</u>, <u>propane</u> and <u>butane</u>.

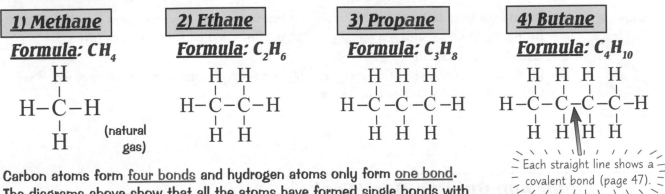

1) Methane
Formula: CH_4

(natural gas)

2) Ethane
Formula: C_2H_6

3) Propane
Formula: C_3H_8

4) Butane
Formula: C_4H_{10}

~ Each straight line shows a ~ covalent bond (page 47). ~

5) Carbon atoms form <u>four bonds</u> and hydrogen atoms only form <u>one bond</u>. The diagrams above show that all the atoms have formed single bonds with as many other atoms as they can — this means they're <u>saturated</u>.

6) Alkanes all have the <u>general formula</u> C_nH_{2n+2}. So if an alkane has 5 carbons, it's got to have $(2 \times 5) + 2 = 12$ hydrogens.

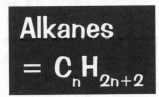

Alkanes $= C_nH_{2n+2}$

Learn the Basic Trends:

1) The <u>shorter</u> the molecules, the <u>less viscous</u> (gloopy) and <u>more runny</u> the hydrocarbon is.
2) The <u>shorter</u> the molecules, the <u>lower the boiling point</u> of the hydrocarbon — so they turn into a gas at a <u>lower temperature</u>.
3) Also, the <u>shorter</u> the molecules, the more <u>flammable</u> (easier to set on fire) the hydrocarbon is.

The Uses Of Hydrocarbons Depend on their Properties

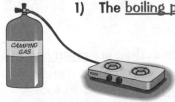

1) The <u>boiling point</u> helps decide what the fraction is used for.

2) The <u>refinery gas fraction</u> has the shortest molecules, so it has the <u>lowest boiling point</u> — in fact it's a gas at room temperature. It's used as <u>bottled gas</u> (e.g. for camping stoves).

3) The <u>petrol</u> fraction has longer molecules, so it has a higher boiling point. Petrol is a <u>liquid</u> which is ideal for storing in the fuel tank of a car. It can flow to the engine where it's easily <u>vaporised</u> (turned to gas) to mix with the air before it is burnt.

Alkane you if you don't learn this...

So <u>short-chain</u> hydrocarbons have a <u>lower boiling point</u> than <u>longer-chain</u> hydrocarbons. They're also <u>less viscous</u> and <u>easier to burn</u>. If you learn the properties of short-chain hydrocarbons, you should be able to work out the properties of longer-chain ones in the exam. These properties decide how they're used.

Using Crude Oil as a Fuel

Nothing as useful as crude oil would be without its problems. No, that would be too good to be true.

Crude Oil Provides an Important Fuel for Modern Life

1) Crude oil fractions make good <u>fuels</u>. For example, they're use to fuel <u>cars</u>, <u>boats</u>, <u>central heating systems</u> in homes and <u>power stations</u>.

2) So, the extraction and use of crude oil is a <u>massive industry</u>.

3) Often, there are <u>alternatives</u> to using crude oil fractions as fuel. E.g. electricity can be generated by <u>nuclear</u> power or <u>wind</u> power, there are <u>ethanol</u>-powered cars, and <u>solar</u> energy can be used to heat water.

4) But things tend to be <u>set up</u> for using oil fractions. For example, cars are designed for <u>petrol or diesel</u> and it's <u>readily available</u>. So crude oil fractions are often the <u>easiest and cheapest</u> thing to use.

5) Crude oil fractions are often <u>more reliable</u> too — e.g. solar and wind power won't work without the right weather conditions.

But it Might Run Out One Day... Eeek

1) Most scientists think that oil will <u>run out</u> — it's a <u>non-renewable fuel</u>. It can't be made again.

2) But no one knows exactly when it'll run out.

3) <u>New oil reserves</u> are discovered from time to time and <u>technology</u> is constantly improving. So, it's now possible to extract oil that was once too <u>difficult</u> or <u>expensive</u> to extract.

4) Some people think we should <u>stop</u> using oil for things like transport <u>now</u>. This is because there are alternative fuels. They think the oil should be saved for things that it's <u>really</u> needed for, like making some medicines.

5) It will take time to <u>develop</u> alternative fuels that will meet all our energy needs (see page 60 for more info). It'll also take time to <u>adapt things</u> so that the fuels can be used on a wide scale. E.g. we might need different kinds of car engines, or special storage tanks built.

6) One alternative is to generate energy from <u>renewable</u> sources — these are sources that <u>won't run out</u>. Examples of renewable energy sources are <u>wind power</u>, <u>solar power</u> and <u>tidal power</u>.

7) So however long oil does last for, it's a good idea to start <u>saving</u> it and finding <u>alternatives</u> now.

Crude Oil is NOT the Environment's Best Friend

1) <u>Oil spills</u> can happen as the oil is being transported by tanker. They are <u>really bad</u> for the local environment. <u>Birds</u> get covered in the stuff and are <u>poisoned</u> as they try to clean themselves. Other creatures, like <u>sea otters</u> and <u>whales</u>, are poisoned too.

2) You have to <u>burn oil</u> to release the energy from it. But burning oil is thought to be a major cause of <u>global warming</u>, <u>acid rain</u> and <u>global dimming</u> — see pages 59 and 60.

If oil alternatives aren't developed, we might get caught short...

Crude oil is <u>really important</u> to our lives. Take <u>petrol</u> for instance — at the first sign of a shortage, people panic. Loads of people dash to the petrol station and start filling up their tanks. This causes a queue, which starts everyone else panicking. I don't know what they'll do when it runs out totally.

Environmental Problems

We burn fuels all the time to release the energy stored inside them.

Burning Fossil Fuels Releases Gases and Particles

1) Power stations burn huge amounts of fossil fuels to make electricity. Cars also burn a lot of fossil fuels.

2) Most fuels, such as crude oil and coal, contain carbon and hydrogen.

3) When fuels are burnt, it's called combustion. During combustion, the carbon and hydrogen are oxidised to carbon dioxide and water vapour. Energy (heat) is also produced.

Pure hydrogen can also be used as a fuel (see next page). It only produces water vapour when burnt.

> hydrocarbon + oxygen → carbon dioxide + water vapour

4) If the fuel contains sulfur impurities, sulfur dioxide is released when the fuel is burnt.

5) Oxides of nitrogen will also form if the fuel burns at a high temperature.

6) When there's plenty of oxygen, all the fuel burns — this is called complete combustion.

7) If there's not enough oxygen, the fuel doesn't burn completely — this is called partial combustion.

8) Partial combustion releases solid particles (called particulates) of soot (carbon). Unburnt fuel and carbon monoxide (a poisonous gas) are also released.

Sulfur Dioxide Causes Acid Rain

1) Sulfur dioxide is one of the gases that causes acid rain.

2) When the sulfur dioxide mixes with clouds it forms dilute sulfuric acid. This then falls as acid rain.

3) Oxides of nitrogen also mix with clouds to form dilute nitric acid. This fall as acid rain too.

4) Acid rain causes lakes to become acidic. This means that many plants and animals die.

5) Acid rain kills trees and damages limestone buildings and ruins stone statues. It's shocking.

You can Reduce Acid Rain by Reducing Sulfur Emissions

1) Most of the sulfur can be removed from fuels before they're burnt.

2) Petrol and diesel are starting to be replaced by low-sulfur versions.

3) Power stations now have Acid Gas Scrubbers to take the sulfur dioxide out of the waste gases before they're released into the atmosphere.

4) The other way of reducing acid rain is simply to reduce our usage of fossil fuels.

Eee, problems, problems — there's always something going wrong...

Pollutants like sulfur dioxide can be carried a long way in the atmosphere. So a country might suffer from acid rain that it didn't cause, which doesn't seem very fair. It's not just up to big industries though — there's lots of things you can do to reduce the amount of fossil fuels burnt. Putting an extra jumper on instead of turning up the heating helps. As does walking places instead of getting a lift.

More Environmental Problems

More doom and gloom on this page I'm afraid... You've got to know it all though.

Increasing Carbon Dioxide Causes Climate Change

1) The level of <u>carbon dioxide</u> in the atmosphere is <u>increasing</u> — because of the large amounts of <u>fossil fuels</u> humans burn.

2) This extra carbon dioxide has caused the average <u>temperature</u> of the Earth to <u>increase</u>. This is known as <u>global warming</u>.

3) Global warming is a type of <u>climate change</u> and causes other types of climate change, e.g. changing rainfall patterns. It could also cause severe <u>flooding</u> due to the polar ice caps melting.

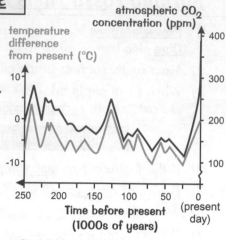

Particles Cause Global Dimming

1) Scientists have been measuring how much <u>sunlight</u> reaches the Earth's surface.

2) In some areas <u>a lot less</u> light has been reaching the surface — they have called this <u>global dimming</u>.

3) Scientists think that it's caused by <u>particles</u> of soot and ash that are produced when <u>fossil fuels</u> are burnt. These particles <u>reflect</u> sunlight back into space.

Alternative Fuels are Being Developed

Some <u>alternative fuels</u> have already been developed. Many of them are <u>renewable</u> fuels so, unlike fossil fuels, they won't run out. However, they all have <u>pros and cons</u>. For example:

<u>ETHANOL</u> can be produced from <u>plant material</u> so is known as a <u>biofuel</u>. It's used to power <u>cars</u> in some places. It's often mixed with petrol to make a better fuel.

<u>PROS</u>: The CO_2 released when it's burnt was taken in by the plant as it grew, so it's 'carbon neutral'. The only other product is <u>water</u>.

<u>CONS</u>: Engines need to be <u>converted</u> before they'll work with ethanol fuels. And ethanol fuel <u>isn't widely available</u>. If farmers grow crops to make ethanol rather than food it could <u>increase food prices</u>.

<u>BIODIESEL</u> is another type of <u>biofuel</u>. It can be produced from <u>vegetable oils</u>. Biodiesel can be mixed with ordinary diesel fuel and used to run a <u>diesel engine</u>.

<u>PROS</u>: Biodiesel is '<u>carbon neutral</u>'. <u>Engines don't</u> need to be <u>converted</u>. It produces much <u>less sulfur dioxide</u> and '<u>particulates</u>' than ordinary diesel or petrol.

<u>CONS</u>: We <u>can't make enough</u> to completely replace diesel. It's <u>expensive</u> to make. It could <u>increase food prices</u> like using more ethanol could (see above).

<u>HYDROGEN GAS</u> can also be used to power vehicles. You get the hydrogen from <u>water</u> but this process uses <u>electrical energy</u>.

<u>PROS</u>: Hydrogen combines with oxygen in the air to form <u>just water</u> — so it's <u>very clean</u>.

<u>CONS</u>: You need a <u>special, expensive engine</u>. Hydrogen <u>isn't widely available</u>. You still need to use <u>energy</u> from <u>another source</u> to make it. Also, hydrogen's hard to <u>store</u>.

Global dimming — romantic lighting all day...

<u>Alternative fuels</u> are the shining light at the end of a long tunnel of problems caused by burning fuels (and I mean long). But <u>nothing's perfect</u> (except maybe my golf swing), so get learning those <u>disadvantages</u>.

Revision Summary for Chemistry 1a

There wasn't anything too bad in this section. A few bits were even quite interesting I reckon.
But you've got to make sure the facts are all firmly fixed in your brain and that you really understand it all.
These questions will let you see what you know and what you don't. If you get stuck on any, you need to
look at that stuff again. Keep going till you can do them all without coming up for air.

1) Sketch an atom. Label the nucleus and the electrons.

2) What are the symbols for: a) calcium, b) carbon, c) sodium?

3)* Which element's properties are more similar to magnesium's: calcium or iron?

4) Work out the electronic structure of sulfur.

5) What type of bonds hold together the atoms in a molecule?

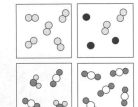

6)* Say which of the diagrams on the right show:
   a) an element   and   b) a compound

7) Write down the word equation showing the thermal decomposition of limestone.

8) What products are produced when calcium carbonate reacts with an acid?

9) Name one thing calcium hydroxide is used for.

10) Name three building materials made from limestone.

11) Plans to develop a limestone quarry and a cement factory on some hills next to your town are
    announced. Describe the views that the following might have:
    a) dog owners
    b) the owner of a cafe

12) What's the definition of an ore?

13) Explain why zinc can be extracted by reduction with carbon but magnesium can't.

14) What is electrolysis?

15) Describe how scrap iron is used to displace copper from solution.

16) What is the name of the method where plants are used to extract metals from soil?

17) Give three reasons why it's good to recycle metal.

18) Give three properties of metals.

19) Briefly describe two problems with metals.

20) What is the problem with using a) iron straight from the blast furnace, b) very pure iron?

21) Give two examples of alloys and say what's in them.

22) What is crude oil made up of? What does fractional distillation do to crude oil?

23) What's the general formula for an alkane?

24) Is a short-chain hydrocarbon more viscous than a long-chain hydrocarbon? Is it more flammable?

25) Name three pollutants released into the atmosphere when fuels are burned.
    What environmental problems are associated with each?

26) List three ways of fuelling cars instead of using petrol or diesel. What are the pros and cons of each?

* Answers on page 108.

Cracking Crude Oil

After the distillation of crude oil (see page 56), you've still got both short and long hydrocarbons. The only difference is that now they're not all mixed together.

Cracking Means Splitting Up Long–chain Hydrocarbons...

1) Long-chain hydrocarbons are thick gloopy liquids like tar which aren't very useful.
2) To make them more useful, they're turned into smaller ones.
3) This is called cracking.
4) Some of the products of cracking are useful as fuels, e.g. petrol for cars.

...by Passing Vapour Over a Hot Catalyst

1) Cracking breaks molecules down by heating them.
2) So cracking is a thermal decomposition reaction.
3) First the hydrocarbon is heated to vaporise it (turn it into a gas).
4) Then the vapour (gas) is passed over a hot catalyst.
5) The long-chain molecules split apart (crack).

See page 48 for another example of a thermal decomposition reaction.

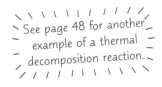

6) Another way of cracking is to mix the gas with steam at a very high temperature.
7) Cracking gives you alkanes and unsaturated hydrocarbons called alkenes...

For more on alkanes see page 57 and for alkenes see page 63.

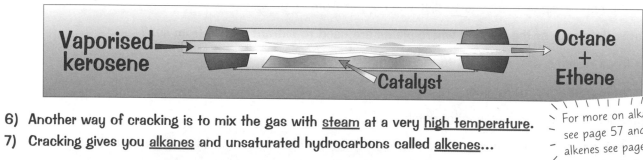

Long-chain hydrocarbon molecule ⟶ Shorter ALKANE molecule + ALKENE

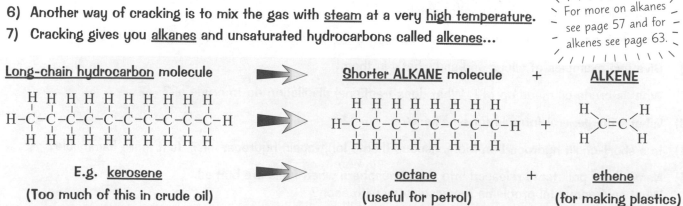

E.g. kerosene ⟶ octane + ethene
(Too much of this in crude oil) (useful for petrol) (for making plastics)

Get cracking — there's a lot to learn...

Crude oil is useful stuff, there's no doubt about it. But don't forget — it has its problems. For example, burning oil is thought to cause climate change, acid rain and global dimming (see page 59 and page 60).

Alkenes and Ethanol

Alkenes are very useful. You can use them to make all sorts of stuff.

Alkenes Have a Carbon=Carbon Double Bond

1) Alkenes are <u>hydrocarbons</u>.
2) They have a <u>double bond</u> between two of the <u>carbon</u> atoms in their chain.
3) This means that they're <u>unsaturated</u>.
4) The first two alkenes are <u>ethene</u> (with two carbon atoms) and <u>propene</u> (three carbon atoms).
5) <u>All alkenes</u> have the general formula: C_nH_{2n}.
6) So the number after the H is <u>always twice</u> the number after the C.

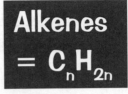

Alkenes
= C_nH_{2n}

1) Ethene

Formula: C_2H_4

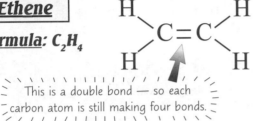

This is a double bond — so each carbon atom is still making four bonds.

2) Propene

Formula: C_3H_6

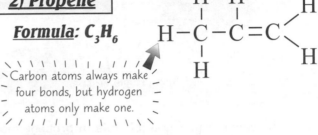

Carbon atoms always make four bonds, but hydrogen atoms only make one.

7) You can <u>test for alkenes</u> by adding them to <u>bromine water</u>.
8) Alkenes turn bromine water from <u>orange</u> to <u>colourless</u>.

bromine water + alkene → colourless

Reacting Ethene With Steam Makes Ethanol

1) <u>Ethene</u> can be <u>hydrated</u> with <u>steam</u> to make <u>ethanol</u>.
2) This reaction needs a <u>catalyst</u> (a catalyst speeds up a reaction).
3) Ethene comes from crude oil, which is a <u>non-renewable resource</u>. So it will run out one day.

Ethanol Can Also Be Made from Renewable Resources

The alcohol in beer isn't made from ethene — it's made by <u>fermentation</u>.

1) Fermentation uses <u>yeast</u> to turn sugar into ethanol.

sugar → carbon dioxide + ethanol

2) This process needs a <u>lower temperature</u> and <u>simpler equipment</u> than using ethene.
3) Another advantage is that sugar is a <u>renewable resource</u>.
4) Also, sugar is <u>grown</u> as a major crop, including in many poorer countries.
5) So ethanol made from sugar is a cheap <u>fuel</u> in countries which don't have much crude oil for making <u>petrol</u>.
6) There are <u>disadvantages</u> though. The ethanol you get from sugar <u>isn't very concentrated</u> (strong). So, it needs to be <u>distilled</u> (as in whisky distilleries). It also needs to be <u>purified</u>.

Make ethanol — not war...

Don't get alk<u>e</u>nes confused with alk<u>a</u>nes — that one letter makes all the difference. Alkenes have a C=C bond, alkanes don't. And remember — alkenes turn <u>bromine water</u> colourless and alkanes don't.

Using Alkenes to Make Polymers

Before we knew how to make <u>polymers</u>, there were no <u>plastic bags</u>. Everyone used string bags for their shopping. Now we have plastic bags that hurt your hands and split halfway home.

Alkenes Can Be Used to Make Polymers

1) Probably the most useful thing you can do with alkenes is <u>polymerisation</u>.

2) This means joining together lots of <u>small alkene molecules</u> (<u>monomers</u>) to form <u>very large molecules</u> (<u>polymers</u>).

3) For example, many <u>ethene</u> molecules can be joined up to produce <u>poly(ethene)</u>.

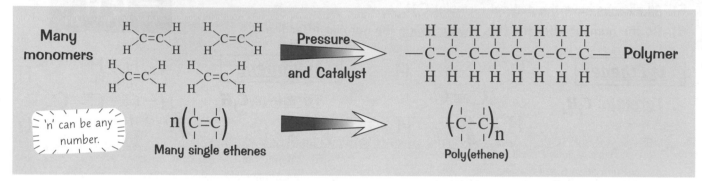

4) In the same way, if you join lots of <u>propene</u> molecules together, you've got <u>poly(propene)</u>.

Polymers Have Lots of Different Uses

1) Poly(ethene) is used to make <u>plastic bags</u> because it's <u>light</u> and <u>stretchy</u>.

2) <u>Elastic</u> polymers are used to make super-stretchy <u>LYCRA®</u> for tights.

3) <u>New uses</u> are developed all the time:
   - <u>Waterproof</u> coatings for fabrics are made of polymers.
   - <u>Polymers</u> are used in <u>tooth fillings</u>.
   - Polymer <u>hydrogel wound dressings</u> keep wounds moist.
   - <u>New biodegradable packaging</u> materials made from polymers and <u>cornstarch</u> are being produced.
   - <u>Memory foam</u> is a polymer that gets <u>softer</u> as it gets <u>warmer</u>. <u>Mattresses</u> made of memory foam mould to your body shape when you lie on them.

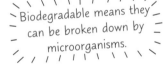
Biodegradable means they can be broken down by microorganisms.

Polymers Are Cheap, but Most Don't Rot — They're Hard to Get Rid Of

1) Most polymers aren't <u>biodegradable</u>, so they <u>don't rot</u>.

2) It's difficult to get rid of them. If you bury them in a landfill site, they'll <u>still</u> be there <u>years later</u>.

3) The best thing is to <u>re-use</u> them as many times as possible and then <u>recycle</u> them if you can.

4) As <u>crude oil</u> gets <u>used up</u> it will get more <u>expensive</u>. This means polymers will also get <u>more expensive</u>.

5) One day there might not be <u>enough</u> oil for fuel AND plastics AND all the other uses.

Revision's like a polymer — you join lots of little facts up...

Polymers are <u>all over the place</u> — and I don't just mean all those plastic bags stuck in trees. Some polymers are <u>natural</u>, e.g. rubber and silk. Others are <u>man-made</u> like polyester and PVC.

Plant Oils

If you squeeze a <u>walnut</u> really hard, some <u>walnut oil</u> will ooze out, which you could use to make <u>walnut mayonnaise</u>. Much better to just buy some oil from the shop though.

We Can Extract Oils from Plants

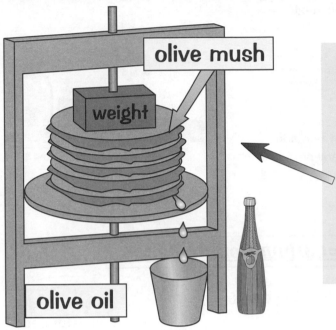

olive mush

weight

olive oil

1) Some <u>fruits</u> and <u>seeds</u> contain a lot of <u>oil</u>. E.g. avocados, olives and Brazil nuts.

2) These oils can be extracted (removed) and used for <u>food</u> or for <u>fuel</u>.

3) <u>Olive oil</u> is a good example. To get the oil out, the plant material is <u>crushed</u>.

4) The next step is to <u>press</u> the crushed plant material between metal plates and squash the oil out (look at the picture).

5) After this, <u>water</u> and other <u>impurities</u> can be removed from the oil.

Vegetable Oils Are Used in Food

1) Vegetable oils provide a lot of <u>energy</u>.

2) They also provide some of the <u>nutrients</u> that our bodies need.

3) For example, oils from seeds contain <u>vitamin E</u>.

Vegetable Oils Have Benefits for Cooking

1) Vegetable oils have <u>higher boiling points</u> than water. This means they can be used to cook foods at higher temperatures and at <u>faster</u> speeds.

2) Cooking with vegetable oil gives food a <u>different flavour</u>. This is down to the oil's own flavour.

3) It's also because the oil '<u>carries</u>' the flavours of the food, making them seem <u>stronger</u>.

4) Using oil to cook food <u>increases</u> the <u>energy</u> we get from eating it. This is because vegetable oil is high in energy.

Don't be silly, that's nut oil, it's a walnut...

Plant oils are pretty fab. All those celebrity chefs would be out of a job without them. And how would you fry up your bacon if it wasn't for good old sunflower oil? That's how you get it nice and crispy and stop it sticking to the pan. It's also jam packed full of <u>nutrients</u> and <u>energy</u> so that should keep hunger locked up till lunch.

Plant Oils

Oils aren't just good for cooking — you can fuel a car with them as well...

Vegetable Oils Can Be Used to Produce Fuels

1) Vegetable oils such as rapeseed oil and soybean oil can be turned into <u>fuels</u>.

2) Vegetable oils provide a lot of <u>energy</u> so they're really good for using as fuels.

3) A very useful fuel made from vegetable oils is called <u>biodiesel</u>.

4) Biodiesel is quite like ordinary <u>diesel</u> fuel — it burns in the same way, so you can use it in a diesel engine.

See page 60 for more about biodiesel.

Unsaturated Oils Contain Carbon=Carbon Double Bonds

1) Oils and fats contain <u>long-chain molecules</u> with lots of <u>carbon</u> atoms.

2) Oils and fats can be <u>saturated</u> or <u>unsaturated</u>.

3) Unsaturated oils contain <u>double bonds</u> between some of the carbon atoms in their carbon chains.

4) So, an unsaturated oil will turn bromine water from orange to <u>colourless</u>.

5) Saturated oils <u>don't</u> contain any carbon=carbon double bonds.

6) So saturated oils <u>won't</u> change bromine water.

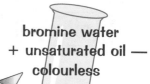

bromine water + unsaturated oil — colourless

Vegetable Oils in Foods Can Affect Health

1) Vegetable oils are normally <u>unsaturated</u>.

2) Animal fats are normally <u>saturated</u>.

3) In general, <u>saturated fats</u> are less healthy than <u>unsaturated fats</u>. This is because <u>saturated</u> fats <u>increase</u> the amount of <u>cholesterol</u> in the blood. Cholesterol can block up the arteries and increase the risk of <u>heart disease</u>.

4) Natural <u>unsaturated</u> fats such as olive oil and sunflower oil <u>decrease</u> blood cholesterol.

5) But, <u>cooking</u> food in any oil, saturated or unsaturated, makes it more <u>fattening</u>.

Double bond — hero of the good fats...

This is tricky stuff. In a nutshell... there are saturated and unsaturated fats, which are <u>mostly</u> bad and good for you (in that order). Then, if you can remember that <u>unsaturated fats</u> have <u>double bonds</u> and how to test for this (pssst they turn bromine water colourless) you'll be on your way to passing that exam.

Emulsions

Emulsions are all over the place in <u>foods</u>, <u>cosmetics</u> and <u>paint</u>. And in exams...

Emulsions Can Be Made from Oil and Water

1) Oils <u>don't dissolve in water</u>. So far so good...

2) But, you can <u>mix</u> an oil with water to make an <u>emulsion</u>.

3) Emulsions are made up of lots of <u>droplets</u> of one liquid <u>suspended</u> in another liquid.

4) You can have an oil-in-water emulsion (oil droplets suspended in water) or a water-in-oil emulsion (water droplets suspended in oil).

Suspended just means the droplets of one liquid are hanging in the other liquid.

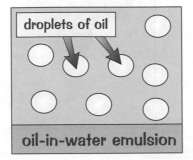

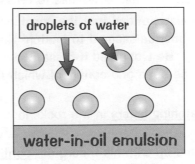

5) Emulsions are <u>thicker</u> than oil and <u>thicker</u> than water. E.g. mayonnaise is an emulsion of sunflower oil and vinegar — it's thicker than both the sunflower oil and the vinegar.

6) Emulsions have <u>lots of uses</u> in <u>food</u> because of their properties — e.g. as salad dressings and in sauces.

Properties describe a substance — e.g. smooth, heavy, shiny or hard.

7) For example, a salad dressing made by shaking olive oil and vinegar together forms an <u>emulsion</u>. This <u>coats</u> salad better than plain oil or plain vinegar.

8) <u>Whipped cream</u> and <u>ice cream</u> are emulsions with an extra ingredient — <u>air</u>. Air is whipped into cream to make it <u>fluffy</u> and <u>frothy</u>. It's mixed into ice cream to make it <u>softer</u> and easier to <u>scoop</u> out of the tub.

9) Emulsions also have <u>non-food uses</u>. Most <u>moisturising lotions</u> are emulsions. They feel smooth and are easy to rub into the skin. Lots of <u>paints</u> are emulsions too.

Emulsifiers Stop Emulsions From Separating Out

1) Mixtures of oil and water (emulsions) naturally want to <u>separate out</u>.

2) Emulsifiers can be added to emulsions to make them more stable and <u>stop</u> them from <u>separating</u> out.

3) Emulsifiers also give emulsions a longer <u>shelf-life</u>.

Texture is how something feels.

4) Emulsifiers let food companies make food that's <u>lower in fat</u> but still has a <u>good texture</u>.

5) One <u>down side</u> is that some people are <u>allergic</u> to certain emulsifiers. For example, <u>egg yolk</u> is often used as an emulsifier. People who are allergic to eggs need to check the ingredients carefully.

Emulsion paint — spread mayonnaise all over the walls...

Before fancy stuff from abroad like olive oil, we fried our bacon and eggs in <u>lard</u>. Mmmm. Lard wouldn't be so good for making salad cream though. Emulsions like salad cream have to be made from shaking up two liquids — tiny droplets of one liquid are 'suspended' or 'hanging' (NOT dissolved) in the other liquid.

Plate Tectonics

The Earth's surface is very <u>crinkly</u> — lots of mountains and valleys. Scientists used to think that these 'wrinkles' were caused by the Earth's surface shrinking as it cooled down after it was made. This theory has now been replaced by one that <u>fits the facts</u> better.

Wegener's Theory of Continental Drift...

1) <u>Wegener</u> noticed that the fossils found on opposite sides of the Atlantic Ocean were <u>almost the same</u>.

2) Other people had noticed this too. But they thought that there had once been <u>land bridges</u> linking the continents — so animals had been able to cross.

3) But Wegener had also noticed that the coastlines of Africa and South America seemed to 'match' like the pieces of a <u>jigsaw</u>. He wondered if these two continents had once been one continent which then split into two.

4) He also found <u>matching layers</u> in the rocks in different countries.

5) Wegener then came up with his theory of "<u>continental drift</u>".

6) His idea was that about 300 million years ago, there had been just one '<u>supercontinent</u>'. He called this huge piece of land Pangaea. Pangaea broke into smaller chunks which moved apart.

7) These smaller chunks make up the continents we have today. Wegener said they were still slowly '<u>drifting</u>' apart.

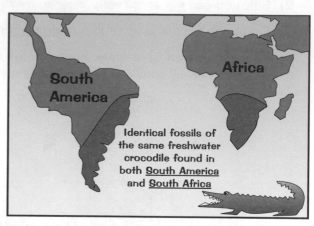

Identical fossils of the same freshwater crocodile found in both <u>South America</u> and <u>South Africa</u>

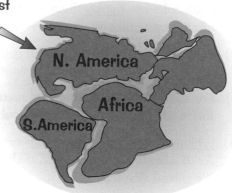

...Wasn't Accepted for Many Years

Most scientists didn't believe Wegener's theory.
His explanation of <u>how</u> the '<u>drifting</u>' happened wasn't very convincing.

1) Wegener thought that the <u>movement</u> of the continents was caused by <u>tidal forces</u> and the Earth's <u>spinning</u>.

2) Other scientists said this was <u>impossible</u>.

3) Wegener had also used <u>dodgy data</u> in his calculations. So his predictions about how fast the continents were moving apart were a bit <u>crazy</u>.

4) Then in the 1950s, scientists investigated the <u>ocean floor</u>. They found <u>new evidence</u> to support Wegener's theory. He wasn't right about everything, but his <u>main idea</u> was <u>correct</u>.

5) By the 1960s, scientists were <u>convinced</u>. We now think the Earth's crust is made of several chunks called <u>tectonic plates</u> which move about.

6) When chunks <u>crash</u> into each other they push the land up and create <u>mountains</u>.

I told you so — but no one ever believes me...

Sadly, Wegener died before his idea was accepted (when hundreds of scientists had to rewrite their textbooks). His story is a classic example of how science moves forward — someone puts forward an idea, everyone else points out why it's nonsense, and in the end the really <u>good</u> ideas are accepted.

The Earth's Structure

Tighten your seat belt for a journey to the centre of the Earth. This page reveals its deepest secrets...

The Earth Has a Crust, Mantle and Core

The Earth is <u>almost round</u> and it has a <u>layered</u> structure.
A bit like a scotch <u>egg</u>. Or a peach.

1) We live on the <u>crust</u>. It's very <u>thin</u> and is surrounded by the <u>atmosphere</u>.

2) Below that is the <u>mantle</u>. The <u>mantle</u> is mostly <u>solid</u>, but it can flow very <u>slowly</u>.

3) Inside the mantle, <u>radioactive decay</u> takes place. This gives out a lot of <u>heat</u>, which causes the mantle to <u>flow</u> in <u>convection currents</u> (in big circles, like in a lava lamp).

4) At the centre of the Earth is the <u>core</u>. We think it's made of <u>iron and nickel</u>.

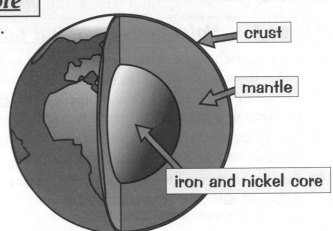

crust

mantle

iron and nickel core

The Earth's Surface is Made Up of Tectonic Plates

1) The crust and the upper part of the mantle are cracked into a number of large pieces called <u>tectonic plates</u>. These plates are a bit like <u>big rafts</u> that 'float' on the mantle.

2) The plates <u>move</u> around. That's because the <u>convection currents</u> in the mantle make the plates <u>drift</u>.

3) The map shows the <u>edges</u> of the plates as they are now, and the <u>directions</u> they're moving in (red arrows).

4) Most of the plates are moving <u>very slowly</u> (a few centimetres a year).

5) Sometimes, the plates move very <u>suddenly</u>, causing an <u>earthquake</u>.

6) <u>Volcanoes</u> and <u>earthquakes</u> often happen where two tectonic plates meet.

You don't need to know the names and locations of the plates.

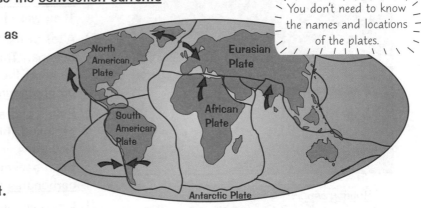

Scientists Can't Predict Earthquakes and Volcanic Eruptions

1) Tectonic plates can stay still for a while and then <u>suddenly</u> jump forwards. It's <u>impossible to know</u> exactly when they'll move.

2) Scientists are trying to find out if there are any <u>clues</u> that an earthquake might happen soon — things like strain in underground rocks. Even with these clues they'll only be able to say an earthquake's <u>likely</u> to happen, not <u>exactly when</u> it'll happen.

3) There are some <u>clues</u> that a volcanic eruption might happen soon. For example, before an eruption, there can be <u>mini-earthquakes</u> near the volcano. But this can be a <u>false alarm</u>.

Plate Tectonics — it's a smashing theory...

Learn the details of the <u>Earth's structure</u>, and make sure you can explain why tectonic plates <u>move</u>.
Then learn the facts about <u>volcanoes</u> and <u>earthquakes</u> and you'll be sorted.

The Evolution of the Atmosphere

For 200 million years or so, the atmosphere has been about how it is now: about 80% nitrogen, 20% oxygen, and small amounts of other gases (mainly carbon dioxide, noble gases and water vapour). But it wasn't always like this. Here's one idea of how the past 4.5 billion years may have gone:

Phase 1 — Volcanoes Gave Out Gases

1) For ages the Earth's surface was molten. It was <u>so hot</u> that any atmosphere just '<u>boiled away</u>' into space.

2) Eventually things cooled down a bit and a <u>thin crust</u> formed, but <u>volcanoes</u> kept erupting.

3) The volcanoes gave out lots of gas — including <u>carbon dioxide</u>, <u>water vapour</u>, <u>methane</u> and <u>ammonia</u>.

4) These gases formed the early atmosphere. It was <u>mostly carbon dioxide</u>, with almost <u>no oxygen</u>. So, it was like the atmospheres of Mars and Venus today.

5) The <u>oceans</u> formed when the water vapour <u>condensed</u>.

Condensed means it's changed from a gas into a liquid.

<u>Holiday report</u>: Not a nice place to be. Take strong walking boots and a good coat.

Phase 2 — Green Plants Evolved and Produced Oxygen

<u>Holiday report</u>: A bit slimy underfoot. Take wellies and a lot of suncream.

1) <u>Green plants</u> and <u>algae</u> grew over most of the Earth. They were happy in the <u>carbon dioxide atmosphere</u>.

2) A lot of the early carbon dioxide <u>dissolved</u> into the oceans. The <u>green plants</u> and <u>algae</u> also absorbed some of the <u>carbon dioxide</u> and <u>produced oxygen</u> by <u>photosynthesis</u>.

3) Plants and algae died and were buried under layers of <u>sediment</u> (bits of plant waste and gravel) along with the skeletons and shells of sea creatures. The <u>carbon</u> inside them became 'locked up' in <u>sedimentary rocks</u> as <u>carbonates</u> and <u>fossil fuels</u>.

4) When we <u>burn</u> fossil fuels, this 'locked up' carbon is released into the atmosphere as <u>carbon dioxide</u>.

Increasing Carbon Dioxide Level Affects the Climate and the Oceans

1) <u>Burning</u> fossil fuels releases carbon dioxide, and we're burning <u>more and more</u> of them...

2) ... so the carbon dioxide level is <u>increasing</u>. This is thought to be <u>changing</u> our planet.

1) An increase in carbon dioxide is causing <u>global warming</u> — a type of <u>climate change</u> (see page 60).

2) The oceans <u>absorb</u> carbon dioxide from the atmosphere. But the extra carbon dioxide we're releasing is making them too <u>acidic</u>. This is bad news for <u>coral</u> and <u>shellfish</u>. Also, in future, the oceans won't be able to absorb <u>any more</u> carbon dioxide.

The atmosphere's evolving — shut the window will you...

No-one was around billions of years ago, so our theories about the atmosphere are just that — theories.

Revision Summary for Chemistry 1b

Cracking alkanes, making mayonnaise, food additives and earthquakes — can they really belong in the same section, I almost hear you ask. Whether you find the topics easy or hard, interesting or dull, you need to learn it all before the exam. Try these questions and see how much you really know:

1)   What is "cracking"?

2)   What's the name of the alkene with two carbon atoms?

3)   What is the general formula for alkenes?

4)   When ethene is hydrated with steam, what substance is formed?

5)   What are polymers?

6)   List four uses of polymers.

7)   Give one problem with using polymers.

8)   Briefly describe how olive oil is extracted.

9)   List two advantages of cooking with oil.

10)   Do unsaturated oils contain any double bonds?

11)   What is an emulsion? Give an example.

12)   Why are emulsifiers needed?

13)   Suggest one problem with adding emulsifiers to food.

14)   Give one reason why Wegener's theory of continental drift wasn't accepted for a long time.

15)   What can be found beneath the Earth's crust?

16)   A scientist places a very heavy marker on the seabed in the middle of the Atlantic ocean. She records the marker's position over a period of four years.
The scientist finds that the marker moves in a straight-line away from its original position. Her measurements are shown in the graph on the right.

a) Explain the process that has caused the marker to move.

b)*How many years did it take for the marker to move 7 cm?

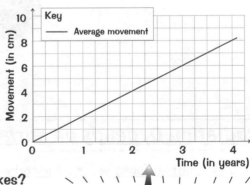

Draw a line across from 7 cm until you hit the line. Then draw a line down and read off the time where your line hits the bottom of the graph.

17)   Why can't scientists accurately predict volcanoes and earthquakes?

18)   Name the two main gases that make up the Earth's atmosphere today.

19)   How did the oceans form?

20)   The burning of fossils fuels is causing a rise in the level of carbon dioxide in the atmosphere. How is this affecting the oceans?

* Answers on page 108

Chemistry 1b — Oils, Earth and Atmosphere

Heat Radiation

Heat energy tends to <u>flow away</u> from a hotter object to its <u>cooler surroundings</u>.

Heat is Transferred in Three Different Ways

1) <u>Heat energy</u> can be transferred (passed on) by <u>conduction</u>, <u>convection</u> or <u>radiation</u>.
2) Most heat in <u>solids</u> is transferred by <u>conduction</u> (see page 73).
3) Most heat in <u>liquids</u> and <u>gases</u> is transferred by <u>convection</u> (see page 74).
4) <u>Heat radiation</u> is the transfer of heat energy by <u>infrared (IR) radiation</u> (see below).

Infrared Radiation — Giving Out of Electromagnetic Waves

1) <u>All objects</u> emit (give out) and absorb (take in) <u>infrared radiation</u>.

2) The <u>hotter</u> an object is, the <u>more</u> infrared radiation it radiates (gives out).

3) An object that's <u>hotter</u> than its surroundings <u>emits more radiation</u> than it <u>absorbs</u> (as it <u>cools</u> down).

4) An object that's <u>cooler</u> than its surroundings <u>absorbs more radiation</u> than it <u>emits</u> (as it <u>warms</u> up).

5) The <u>bigger the temperature difference</u>, the <u>faster heat is transferred</u> between an object and its surroundings.

6) You can <u>feel</u> this <u>heat radiation</u> if you stand near something <u>hot</u> like a fire.

(recently parked car)

Radiation Depends on Surface Colour and Texture

1) <u>Dark</u>, <u>matt surfaces</u> are <u>good absorbers</u> and <u>good emitters</u> of infrared radiation.

2) <u>Light</u>, <u>shiny surfaces</u> are <u>poor absorbers</u> and <u>poor emitters</u> of infrared radiation. They are also <u>good reflectors</u> of infrared radiation.

Matt means non-shiny.

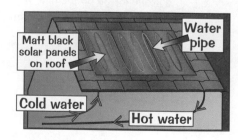

3) <u>Solar hot water panels</u> usually have <u>water pipes</u> under a <u>black surface</u>.

4) <u>Radiation</u> from the Sun is <u>absorbed</u> by the <u>black surface</u> to <u>heat the water</u> in the pipes.

5) This water can be used for <u>washing</u> or pumped to <u>radiators</u> to heat the building.

Feelin' hot hot hot...

If a surface is a good emitter, that <u>doesn't</u> mean it is a poor absorber. Oh no. A surface is either <u>good</u> at both <u>emitting</u> and <u>absorbing</u> radiation, or <u>poor</u> at both <u>emitting</u> and <u>absorbing</u> radiation. Got that? Good, good.

Kinetic Theory and Conduction

Kinetic theory is just a fancy way of describing how particles <u>move</u> in <u>solids</u>, <u>liquids</u> and <u>gases</u>. Read on...

Kinetic Theory Can Explain the Three States of Matter

1) The <u>three states of matter</u> are <u>solid</u> (e.g. ice), <u>liquid</u> (e.g. water) and <u>gas</u> (e.g. water vapour).

2) The <u>particles</u> in solids, liquids and gases are all <u>the same</u> — but have <u>different</u> amounts of <u>energy</u>.

a) <u>Strong forces</u> of attraction (a pull) hold the particles <u>close together</u>.
b) The particles are arranged in a <u>pattern</u>.
c) The particles <u>don't</u> have much <u>energy</u> so they <u>can</u> only <u>vibrate</u> a little.

Vibrate just means they jiggle about.

a) There are <u>weaker forces</u> of attraction between the particles.
b) The particles are <u>close together</u>, but can <u>move past each other</u>.
c) They have <u>more energy</u> than the particles in a <u>solid</u> — they move in <u>all directions</u> at <u>low speeds</u>.

a) There are <u>almost no</u> forces of attraction between the particles.
b) The particles have <u>more energy</u> than those in <u>liquids</u> and <u>solids</u>.
c) They are <u>free to move</u> in <u>any direction</u> and move at <u>high speeds</u>.

3) When you <u>heat</u> something, you give its particles <u>more energy</u>. This means the particles will <u>vibrate</u> or <u>move faster</u>. This is what eventually causes <u>solids</u> to <u>melt</u> and <u>liquids</u> to <u>boil</u>.

Conduction of Heat — happens Mainly in Solids

CONDUCTION OF HEAT is where <u>VIBRATING PARTICLES</u> pass on their <u>ENERGY</u> to the <u>PARTICLES NEXT TO THEM</u>.

1) Materials with their particles <u>close together</u> are <u>conductors</u>. This means they <u>bang into</u> each other <u>often</u> and <u>pass energy quickly</u> between them.

2) Materials with <u>large spaces</u> between their particles conduct heat much more <u>slowly</u> — these materials are <u>insulators</u>.

Metals are Good Conductors Because of Their Free Electrons

Free Electrons

1) <u>Metals conduct</u> so well because they have electrons that are <u>free to move</u> inside the metal.

2) At the <u>hot end</u> the electrons move <u>faster</u> and collide with other <u>free electrons</u>, <u>transferring energy</u>. These other electrons then pass on their extra energy to other electrons, etc.

Gas particles are crazy dancers — they just love to move about...
Remember, the particles in conductors are <u>close together</u>, and in insulators they have <u>large spaces</u> between them.

Convection

Gases and liquids transfer heat by convection. And it's all thanks to our friend, the particle...

Convection of Heat — Liquids and Gases Only

> CONVECTION happens when the particles with the most energy MOVE from the HOTTER PLACE to the COOLER PLACE — AND TAKE THEIR HEAT ENERGY WITH THEM.

The Immersion Heater Example

1) Heat is transferred from the heater coils to the water by conduction (see page 73).

2) The particles near the coils get more energy, so they start moving around faster.

3) This means there's more distance between them, i.e. the water expands (gets bigger) and becomes less dense.

4) A lower density means that the hotter water will rise above the denser water.

5) As the hot water rises it moves the colder water out of the way, making it sink towards the heater coils.

6) This cold water is then heated by the coils and rises — and so it goes on.

7) You end up with convection currents going up, round and down, moving the heat through the water.

8) The hot water ends up at the top of the tank, and the cooler water ends up at the bottom.

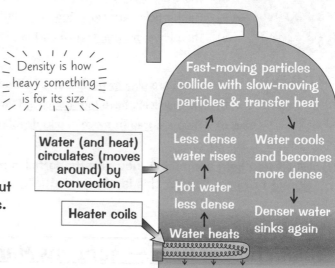

Density is how heavy something is for its size.

Water (and heat) circulates (moves around) by convection

Heater coils

Fast-moving particles collide with slow-moving particles & transfer heat

Less dense water rises

Hot water less dense

Water heats

Water cools and becomes more dense

Denser water sinks again

> CONVECTION CURRENTS are all about CHANGES IN DENSITY.

The Radiator Example

1) Heating a room with a radiator uses convection currents too.

2) Hot, less dense air by the radiator rises and denser, cooler air flows to replace it.

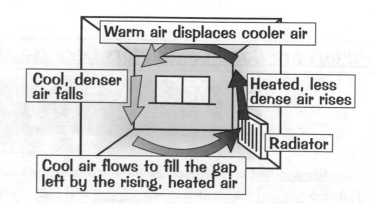

Warm air displaces cooler air

Cool, denser air falls

Heated, less dense air rises

Radiator

Cool air flows to fill the gap left by the rising, heated air

---

The rise and fall of liquids and gases — it's a sad story...

Remember that when the particles in a gas or liquid gain energy they start to move around faster. As they move faster, the liquid or gas becomes less dense and so it rises. Wheeeeeeee...

Condensation and Evaporation

Here are a couple more things about particles in gases and liquids you need to think about.

Condensation is When Gas Turns to Liquid

1) When a gas cools, the particles in the gas slow down and lose energy.

2) The attractive forces between the particles pull them closer together.

3) If gas particles get close enough together and the temperature is cold enough, then condensation happens and the gas becomes a liquid.

4) Water vapour in the air condenses when it touches a cold surface, e.g. drinks glasses.

Evaporation is When Liquid Turns to Gas

1) Evaporation is when particles escape from a liquid.

2) Particles near the surface of a liquid can escape and become gas particles if:

- The particles are travelling in the right direction to escape the liquid.
- The particles have enough energy to break free from the attractive forces of the other particles in the liquid.

3) The particles with the most energy are most likely to evaporate from the liquid.

4) When the particles with the most energy evaporate, the average energy of the particles left behind decreases.

5) This means the temperature of the liquid left behind falls — the liquid cools.

The Speed of Evaporation and Condensation can Vary

The RATE (SPEED) OF EVAPORATION will be faster if the...

- TEMPERATURE of the liquid is higher.
- DENSITY of the liquid is lower.
- SURFACE AREA of the liquid is larger — more of the particles will be closer to the surface of the liquid so more can escape.
- AIRFLOW over the liquid is greater — the air around the liquid will change more often. So there will be less liquid in the air, making it easier for evaporation to happen.

The RATE (SPEED) OF CONDENSATION will be faster if the...

- TEMPERATURE of the surface the gas touches is lower.
- SURFACE AREA of the surface the gas touches is larger.

A little less condensation, a little more action...

The people who make adverts for drinks know what customers like to see — condensation on the outside of a can or bottle. It makes the drink look nice and cold and refreshing. Mmmm. Very clever of them...

Rate of Heat Transfer

There are loads of things that affect the rate of heat transfer (how quickly heat is transferred).

The Rate an Object Transfers Heat Energy Depends on...

Surface Area and Volume

1) Heat is radiated (sent out) from the surface of an object.

2) The bigger the surface area, the more infrared waves can be emitted from the surface (or absorbed by the surface). This means heat transfer is quicker.

3) Radiators have large surface areas to increase the amount of heat they transfer.

4) Car and motorbike engines often have 'fins' to increase the surface area so heat is radiated away quicker. So the engine cools quicker.

5) Heat sinks are devices designed to transfer heat away from objects they're in contact with (touching), e.g. computer parts. They also have fins so they can radiate heat as quickly as possible.

6) If two objects at the same temperature have the same surface area but different volumes, the object with the smaller volume will cool more quickly.

Cooling fins on engines increase surface area to speed up cooling.

> **Example**
>
> Shape A:
> Surface area = **24 cm²**
> Volume = **8 cm³**
>
>   2 cm / 2 cm / 2 cm
>
> 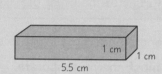 1 cm / 5.5 cm / 1 cm
>
> Shape B:
> Surface area = **24 cm²**
> Volume = **5.5 cm³**
>
> Shape A and B have the same surface area — but shape B has a smaller volume.
> So, Shape B will lose heat quicker than Shape A.

The Material of the Object and What it's Touching

1) Objects made from conductors (see p.73) will transfer heat more quickly than objects made from insulators.

2) Heat will be conducted away much faster from an object in contact with a conductor than an insulator.

Metal is a conductor — so a metal spoon will conduct heat away quickly from the hot drink.

Plastic is an insulator — so a plastic spoon will conduct heat away slower from the hot drink than the metal spoon.

3) The bigger the temperature difference, the faster heat is transferred between the object and what it's touching.

I'd rate this page pretty highly...

So remember, the rate that an object transfers heat energy depends on its surface area and volume, what it's made of and what it's touching. Lots of information to get your head around, but it's really important stuff folks.

Rate of Heat Transfer

If we know the things that <u>increase</u> the rate of <u>heat transfer</u>, then we can <u>cleverly</u> design things so that we <u>reduce</u> this <u>heat transfer</u>...

Vacuum Flasks are Designed to Reduce Heat Transfer

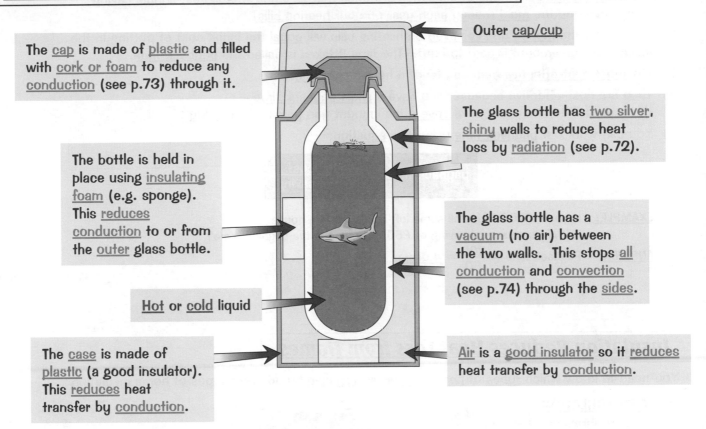

The <u>cap</u> is made of <u>plastic</u> and filled with <u>cork or foam</u> to reduce any <u>conduction</u> (see p.73) through it.

Outer <u>cap/cup</u>

The glass bottle has <u>two silver</u>, <u>shiny</u> walls to reduce heat loss by <u>radiation</u> (see p.72).

The bottle is held in place using <u>insulating foam</u> (e.g. sponge). This <u>reduces conduction</u> to or from the <u>outer</u> glass bottle.

The glass bottle has a <u>vacuum</u> (no air) between the two walls. This stops <u>all</u> <u>conduction</u> and <u>convection</u> (see p.74) through the <u>sides</u>.

<u>Hot</u> or <u>cold</u> liquid

The <u>case</u> is made of <u>plastic</u> (a good insulator). This <u>reduces</u> heat transfer by <u>conduction</u>.

<u>Air</u> is a <u>good insulator</u> so it <u>reduces</u> heat transfer by <u>conduction</u>.

Humans and Animals Have Ways of Controlling Heat Transfer

Animals do this with their fur.

1) In the <u>cold</u>, the hairs on your skin 'stand up' and trap a <u>thicker</u> layer of <u>insulating air</u> around your body. This reduces the amount of heat you lose by <u>convection</u> and <u>conduction</u>.

2) <u>Coats</u> and <u>duvets</u> also keep us warm by trapping an <u>insulating layer</u> of air — which <u>reduces</u> convection and conduction.

3) Generally, animals in <u>warm</u> climates have <u>larger</u> ears than those in <u>cold</u> climates to help <u>control</u> heat transfer.

For example, Arctic foxes have <u>small ears</u>, with a small surface area to reduce <u>heat loss</u> by <u>radiation</u>.

Desert foxes on the other hand have <u>huge ears</u> with a large surface area so they can <u>lose heat</u> by <u>radiation</u> and keep cool.

Don't call me 'Big Ears' — call me 'Large Surface Area'...

If you're asked about heat transfer in the exam, you must <u>always</u> say how heat is transferred at any point — either <u>conduction</u>, <u>convection</u> or <u>radiation</u>. You've got to show the examiners that you know your stuff.

Energy Efficiency in the Home

There are lots of things you can do to a building to <u>reduce</u> the amount of <u>heat energy that escapes</u>.

Effectiveness and Cost-effectiveness are Not the Same Thing...

1) The <u>most effective</u> methods of insulation are ones that give you the biggest <u>annual saving</u> (they save you the <u>most</u> money <u>each year</u> on your <u>heating bills</u>).

2) Eventually, the <u>money you've saved</u> on heating bills will <u>equal</u> the initial cost of putting in the insulation (the amount it cost to buy). The time it takes is called the <u>payback time</u>.

3) The <u>most cost-effective</u> methods tend to be the <u>cheapest</u>.

4) They are cost-effective because they have a <u>short payback time</u> — this means the money you save <u>covers</u> the amount you <u>paid</u> really <u>quickly</u>.

5) You can work out <u>payback time</u> using this <u>equation</u>:

$$\text{payback time} = \frac{\text{initial cost}}{\text{annual saving}}$$

<u>EXAMPLE:</u> It costs £200 to install some loft insulation in a house.
If it gives an annual saving of £50, how long is the payback time?

<u>ANSWER:</u> Payback time = $\frac{200}{50}$ = <u>4 years</u>

Insulation Reduces Heat Loss from Homes

You need to know which <u>types</u> of <u>heat transfer</u> are <u>reduced</u> by different types of home insulation.

1) <u>LOFT INSULATION</u> — a thick layer of fibreglass wool laid out across the whole loft floor reduces <u>conduction</u> and <u>radiation</u> into the roof space from the ceiling.

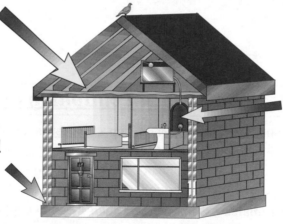

2) <u>CAVITY WALL INSULATION</u> — foam squirted into the gap between the bricks reduces <u>convection</u> and <u>radiation</u> across the gap.

3) <u>HOT WATER TANK JACKET</u> — insulating materials, e.g. fibreglass wool, reduce <u>conduction</u> and <u>radiation</u>.

U-Values Show How Fast Heat can Transfer Through a Material

1) <u>Heat</u> transfers <u>faster</u> through materials with <u>higher U-values</u> than through materials with low U-values.

2) So the <u>better the insulator</u> (see page 73) the <u>lower</u> the U-value.

3) For example, the U-value of a <u>duvet</u> is about <u>0.75 W/m²K</u>, whereas the U-value of <u>loft insulation material</u> is around <u>0.15 W/m²K</u>.

It's payback time...

Make sure you know what's meant by effectiveness and cost-effectiveness. <u>Effective methods</u> of insulation are ones that save you a <u>lot of money</u> on your bills. <u>Cost-effective</u> methods pay for themselves pretty <u>quickly</u>.

Specific Heat Capacity

Specific heat capacity sounds a bit scary — but be brave and read on...

Specific Heat Capacity Tells You How Much Energy Stuff Can Store

1) It takes more heat energy to increase the temperature of some materials than others.

2) Materials which need to gain lots of energy to warm up also release loads of energy when they cool down again. They can 'store' a lot of heat.

3) The measure of how much energy a substance (material) can store is called its specific heat capacity.

> Specific heat capacity is the amount of energy needed to raise the temperature of 1 kg of a substance by 1 °C.

There's a Handy Formula for Specific Heat Capacity

1) You'll have to do calculations involving specific heat capacity. This is the equation to learn:

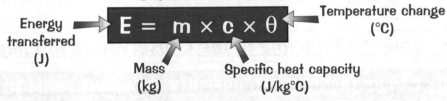

Energy transferred (J)

$$E = m \times c \times \theta$$

Temperature change (°C)

Mass (kg)

Specific heat capacity (J/kg°C)

> **EXAMPLE:** How much energy is needed to heat 2 kg of water from 10 °C to 100 °C? (Water has a specific heat capacity of 4200 J/kg°C.)
>
> **ANSWER:** Energy needed = 2 × 4200 × (100 – 10)
> = 2 × 4200 × 90 = <u>756 000 J</u>

2) In the exam, you might have to work out something other than the energy transferred.

3) Don't panic, you won't have to rearrange the equation yourself — you'll be given it already rearranged. All you need to do is put in the right numbers.

Heaters Have High Heat Capacities to Store Lots of Energy

1) The materials used in heaters usually have high specific heat capacities.

2) Water has a really high specific heat capacity. It's also a liquid, so it can easily be pumped around in pipes — ideal for central heating systems in buildings.

3) Electric storage heaters store heat energy at night and then release it during the day. They store the heat using concrete or bricks, which have a high specific heat capacity.

4) Some heaters are filled with oil. Oil has a lower specific heat capacity than water — this means they're often not as good as water heating systems.

I've just eaten five sausages — I have a high specific meat capacity...

I'm sure you'll agree that this isn't the most exciting part of GCSE physics — but it is likely to come up in your exam. Sadly you just have to get that equation learnt. Then reward yourself with a biscuit. Or two. Yay.

Energy Transfer

Heat is just one type of energy, but there are lots more:

Learn These Nine Types of Energy

1) ELECTRICAL Energy.................................... — whenever a current flows.
2) LIGHT Energy... — from the Sun, light bulbs, etc.
3) SOUND Energy.. — from loudspeakers or anything noisy.
4) KINETIC Energy, or MOVEMENT Energy......... — anything that's moving has it.
5) NUCLEAR Energy...................................... — released only from nuclear reactions.
6) THERMAL Energy or HEAT Energy............... — flows from hot objects to colder ones.
7) GRAVITATIONAL POTENTIAL Energy............... — possessed by anything which can fall.
8) ELASTIC POTENTIAL Energy...................... — stretched springs, elastic, rubber bands, etc.
9) CHEMICAL Energy..................................... — possessed by foods, fuels, batteries etc.

The last three types of energy above are all types of stored energy. The energy is not obviously doing anything — it's kind of waiting to happen, i.e. waiting to be turned into one of the other forms.

You Need to Know the Principle of the Conservation of Energy:

ENERGY CAN BE TRANSFERRED USEFULLY FROM ONE FORM TO ANOTHER, STORED OR DISSIPATED — BUT IT CAN NEVER BE CREATED OR DESTROYED.

Dissipated is a fancy way of saying the energy is spread out and unusable.

falling object

Gravitational Potential → Kinetic

Another important thing which you need to learn is this one:

Energy is only useful when it can be transferred from one form to another.

Examples of Energy Transfers

1) Electrical Devices, e.g. televisions: Electrical energy ⟹ Light, sound and heat energy
2) Batteries: Chemical energy ⟹ Electrical and heat energy
3) Electrical Generation, e.g. wind turbines: Kinetic energy ⟹ Electrical and heat energy
4) Potential Energy, e.g. firing a bow and arrow: Elastic potential energy ⟹ Kinetic and heat energy

Energy can't be created or destroyed — only talked about a lot...

Chemical energy → kinetic energy;   Electrical energy → kinetic energy;   Light energy → headache.
(me eating)   (me typing)   (my computer)   (printing machine)   (you reading this) (probably)

Efficiency of Machines

More! More! Tell me more about energy transfers please! OK, since you insist:

Most Energy Transfers Involve Some Losses, Often as Heat

1) <u>Useful devices</u> are only <u>useful</u> because they can <u>transform</u> (change) <u>energy</u> from <u>one form</u> to <u>another</u>.

2) When they do, some of the useful <u>input energy</u> (total energy in) is always <u>wasted</u>, often as <u>heat</u>.

3) The <u>more energy</u> that is transformed into <u>useful</u> <u>energy</u>, the <u>more efficient</u> the device is.

4) This <u>energy flow diagram</u> is pretty much the same for <u>all devices</u>.

5) A device is a <u>machine</u> which turns <u>one type of energy</u> into <u>another</u>.

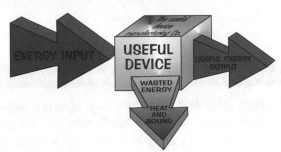

You Need to Know How to Work Out the Efficiency of a Device

Energy is totally in this season.

1) The <u>efficiency</u> of any device is defined as:

$$\text{Efficiency} = \frac{\text{Useful Energy out}}{\text{Total Energy in}}$$

EXAMPLE: A TV has an input energy of 220 J. It gives out 5 J of light energy, 2 J of sound energy and 213 J as heat energy. Work out the efficiency of the TV.

ANSWER: The light and sound energy are useful, but the heat energy is wasted energy. So:

$$\text{Efficiency} = \frac{5 + 2}{220} = \frac{7}{220} = 0.0318 \quad \text{or} \quad 3.18\%$$

multiply the decimal by 100 to get it as a percentage

2) You might not know the <u>energy</u> in and out of a machine, but you can <u>still</u> calculate the machine's efficiency as long as you know the <u>power</u> put in and given out:

$$\text{Efficiency} = \frac{\text{Useful Power out}}{\text{Total Power in}}$$

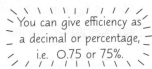

You can give efficiency as a decimal or percentage, i.e. 0.75 or 75%.

Useful Energy Out Isn't Usually Equal to Total Energy In

1) All appliances <u>waste</u> some energy.

<u>No</u> device is 100% efficient and the <u>wasted energy</u> is usually <u>spread out</u> as <u>heat</u>.

2) This heat is <u>transferred</u> to <u>cooler</u> surroundings, which then become <u>warmer</u>.

3) As the heat is <u>transferred</u> to cooler surroundings, the <u>energy</u> dissipates — so it becomes <u>less useful</u>.

Don't waste your energy — turn the TV off while you revise...

And for <u>10 bonus points</u>, calculate the efficiency of this machine:
Loudspeaker — input energy 35 J, sound energy given out 0.5 J, heat energy given out 34.5 J. Answers p.108.

Efficiency of Machines

By using <u>efficient</u> devices, you can <u>cut down</u> the amount of <u>energy</u> you use to do something (your '<u>energy consumption</u>'). But there are <u>other factors</u> to think about when buying a device...

You Need to Think About Cost-Effectiveness and Efficiency...

...When Choosing Appliances

> Appliances are machines usually found in your home that transfer electrical energy into other types of energy.

Example: Replacing Old Appliances with Newer Energy-Efficient Ones

1) <u>New</u>, <u>efficient</u> appliances are <u>cheaper</u> to run than <u>older</u>, <u>less efficient</u> appliances. But new appliances can be <u>expensive</u> to <u>buy</u>.
2) You've got to work out if it's <u>cost-effective</u> (page 78) to buy a <u>new appliance</u>.
3) To work out how <u>cost-effective</u> a new appliance will be you need to work out its <u>payback time</u> (p78).

Example: Light Bulbs

1) A <u>low-energy</u> bulb is about <u>4 times as efficient</u> as an <u>ordinary</u> light bulb.
2) <u>Energy-efficient</u> light bulbs are more <u>expensive</u> to buy but they <u>last much longer</u>.
3) If an energy-saving light bulb cost £3 and saved £12 of energy a year, its <u>payback time</u> (see page 78) would be <u>3 months</u>.
4) Energy-saving light bulbs are normally <u>more cost-effective</u> than ordinary bulbs.
5) <u>LED light bulbs</u> are even <u>more efficient</u> than <u>low-energy</u> bulbs, and can <u>last even longer</u>.
6) But they are <u>more</u> expensive to buy and <u>don't</u> give out as <u>much light</u> as the other two types of bulb.

Sometimes 'Waste' Energy Can Actually Be Useful

1) <u>Heat exchangers</u> reduce the amount of <u>heat energy</u> that is 'lost'.
2) They do this by pumping a <u>cool liquid</u> through the <u>escaping heat</u> — the liquid <u>heats up</u>.
3) The <u>heat energy</u> of the liquid can then be <u>transferred</u> into a form of energy that's useful again.

Example: Car Heat Exchanger

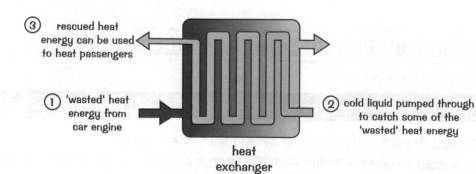
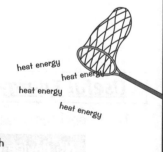

③ rescued heat energy can be used to heat passengers

① 'wasted' heat energy from car engine

② cold liquid pumped through to catch some of the 'wasted' heat energy

heat exchanger

Let there be light — and a bit of wasted heat...

The thing about <u>loss of energy</u> is it's <u>always the same</u> — it <u>almost always disappears as heat</u> and sound, and even the sound ends up as heat pretty quickly. What a waste. I'm off to have a cup of tea to cheer myself up.

Energy Transformation Diagrams

Crikey, that's a long title. Here's what those energy transformation diagrams are all about...

The Thickness of the Arrow Represents the Amount of Energy

1) Energy transformation (Sankey) diagrams make it easy to see how much of the input energy is being used usefully and how much is being wasted.

2) The thicker the arrow, the more energy it represents.

3) You see a big thick arrow going in, then smaller arrows going off it to show the different energy transformations taking place.

4) You can have either a little sketch or a properly detailed diagram (see below).

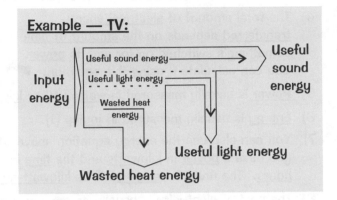

Example — TV:

Input energy

Useful sound energy
Useful light energy
Wasted heat energy

Useful sound energy

Useful light energy

Wasted heat energy

Example — Sankey Diagram for a Simple Motor:

HERE'S THE SKETCH VERSION:

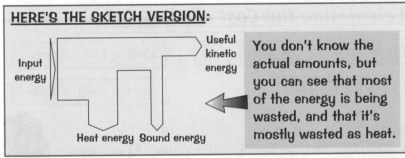

Input energy

Useful kinetic energy

Heat energy   Sound energy

You don't know the actual amounts, but you can see that most of the energy is being wasted, and that it's mostly wasted as heat.

AND HERE'S THE DETAILED ONE:

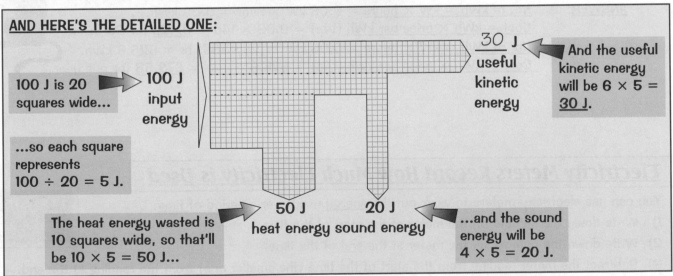

100 J is 20 squares wide...

100 J input energy

...so each square represents 100 ÷ 20 = 5 J.

The heat energy wasted is 10 squares wide, so that'll be 10 × 5 = 50 J...

50 J heat energy

20 J sound energy

30 J useful kinetic energy

And the useful kinetic energy will be 6 × 5 = 30 J.

...and the sound energy will be 4 × 5 = 20 J.

Skankey diagrams — to represent the smelliness of your socks...

If they ask you to draw your own Sankey diagram in the exam, and don't give you any numbers, a sketch is all they'll expect. Just give a rough idea of where the energy goes. Hooray for drawing pictures in exams.

The Cost of Electricity

Electricity's great — you can power all sorts of gadgets with it. But it'll cost you...

Kilowatt-hours (kWh) are "UNITS" of Energy

1) Anything that needs electricity to work is an electrical appliance.

2) All electrical appliances change (or transfer) electrical energy into other forms of energy (see page 80).

3) Power tells you how fast something transfers energy.

4) The total amount of electrical energy transferred depends on the amount of time something's switched on for and its power. You can calculate it using this equation:

> ENERGY TRANSFERRED = POWER x TIME
> (J)   (W)   (s)

5) Power is usually measured in watts (W) or kilowatts (kW). 1 kW = 1000 W.

6) Energy is usually measured in joules (J).

7) You can also use the energy equation above when you have a power in kilowatts and the time in hours. The units for energy will be kilowatt-hours.

> 1 KILOWATT-HOUR is the amount of electrical energy used by a 1 kW appliance left on for 1 HOUR.

8) The cost of electricity is usually an amount per kilowatt-hour, e.g. 13p per kWh.

The Two Easy Formulas for Calculating the Cost of Electricity

ENERGY transferred (kWh) = POWER (in kW) × TIME (in hours)	kWh = kW × hours
COST = Energy transferred (kWh) × PRICE per kWh	Cost = kWh × Price

EXAMPLE: Electricity costs 14p per kWh.
    Find the cost of leaving a 60 W light bulb on for: a) 30 minutes   b) one year.

ANSWER: a)   No. of kWh = kW × hours = 0.06 kW × ½ hr = 0.03 kWh.
        Cost = kWh × price per kWh (14p) = 0.03 × 14p = 0.42p for 30 mins.

    b)   No. of kWh = kW × hours = 0.06 kW × (24×365) hr = 525.6 kWh.
        Cost = kWh × price per kWh (14p) = 525.6 × 14p = £73.58 for one year.

Electricity Meters Record How Much Electricity is Used

You can use electricity meters to work out the energy used over a period of time.

1) Write down the number on the meter at the start of the time.

2) Write down the number on the meter at the end of the time.

3) Subtract the meter reading from the start of the time (the smaller one) from the reading at the end.

> 1 3 5 9 2 . 3 2 kWh
> Electricity Meter

500 kWh doesn't mean much to anyone — £70 is far more real...

Don't worry about remembering the cost of electricity — you'll get told it in the exam if you need it. Make sure you get to grips with the equations, and don't let kilowatt-hours scare you — they're just a fancy-sounding energy unit.

Choosing Electrical Appliances

Sadly, this isn't about what <u>colour</u> MP3 player to get. But you've got to know it I'm afraid...

Sometimes You Have a Choice of Electrical Equipment...

1) Before you decide which one to use, you need to look at the <u>advantages and disadvantages</u> (good and bad points) of each.

2) From that you can work out which one is <u>most suitable</u> (the best) to use.

- How <u>cheap</u>/<u>expensive</u> is it to buy?
- How much <u>energy</u> will it <u>use</u>/<u>waste</u>?
- Will it be <u>cheap to run</u>?
- <u>Size</u> and <u>shape</u> — will it fit where you want it to? Can it be easily carried?
- Can it be used when there <u>isn't</u> an <u>electricity supply</u>, e.g. when camping?
- How <u>well</u> will it do the job?

E.G. MAINS FANS AND HAND-HELD FANS	Mains-powered fan	Hand-held battery-powered fan 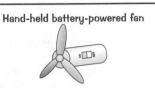
Cost to buy	£10-£300	£1-£15
Cost to run	Fairly cheap	Quite expensive
Size	A range of sizes — can be very large.	small
Can it be used in places without electricity?	No	Yes
Can it be used to cool large areas?	Yes	No

3) So... if you were picking a fan to cool a work place — a <u>mains-powered fan</u> would be best. They can be <u>very large</u> and <u>fairly cheap</u> to run, and can be used to <u>cool entire rooms</u>.

4) Also, workers might need to use their <u>hands</u> to do their job, so <u>hand-held</u> fans wouldn't be very useful.

5) If you wanted a fan to cool you while <u>travelling</u>, a <u>hand-held fan</u> would be the best choice.

6) You might <u>not</u> be near an <u>electricity supply</u> while travelling, and carrying around a <u>huge</u> fan would be annoying.

7) In the exam, you might be asked to use data to <u>compare two appliances</u>. For example, you might need to calculate the <u>efficiency</u> (p.81) and <u>cost</u> of running devices — then you can pick the best one.

People's Lives are Affected by Access to Electricity

1) Electrical devices <u>transform electrical energy</u> into <u>other</u> useful types of energy (see p.80).

2) Here in the UK, we rely a lot on electricity to keep us <u>safe</u> and <u>healthy</u>.

3) For example, electric lighting is not only <u>useful</u>, but it can also help make places <u>safe</u> at night.

4) Many people in the world's <u>poorest</u> countries <u>don't</u> have an <u>electricity supply</u>. This has a <u>big effect</u> on their lives, in particular their <u>health</u>.

5) <u>Refrigerators</u> use electricity to keep <u>food fresh</u> for longer. Refrigerators are also used to store <u>vaccines</u>.

6) Without the electricity for refrigeration, food can <u>go bad quickly</u> and cause <u>illness</u> if eaten. Also, vaccines <u>can't be stored</u> or taken to where they're needed — so people <u>can't be protected against diseases</u>.

7) <u>Hospitals</u> can use a lot of electricity, e.g. for <u>X-ray</u> machines. If there is <u>no electricity</u> for these sorts of machines, it can be much more difficult to <u>diagnose</u> and <u>treat</u> medical problems.

8) Electricity is also important for getting and sending <u>news</u> and <u>information</u> e.g. via the <u>internet</u> or <u>telephones</u>.

Decisions, decisions...

When choosing appliances just use your common sense. Don't panic — pick out the <u>good</u> and <u>bad</u> points of the appliances before you make your decision. And make sure you can talk about <u>why</u> electricity is <u>so important</u>.

Revision Summary for Physics 1a

Right, it's crunch time — have a go at these questions to see how much has gone in...

1) Describe the three ways that heat energy can be transferred.

2) Explain why solar hot water panels have a matt black surface.

3) Describe the arrangement and movement of the particles in solids.

4) What is the name of the process where vibrating particles pass on energy to the particles next to them?

5) Describe how the heat from the heating coil at the bottom of an electric kettle is transferred throughout the water in the kettle. What is this process called?

6) How do the densities of liquids and gases change as you heat them?

7) What happens to the particles of a gas as it turns to a liquid?

8) What is the name given to the process where a gas turns to a liquid?

9) The two designs of car engine shown are made from the same material. Which engine will transfer heat quicker? Explain why.
Engine A   Engine B

10) Describe two features of a vacuum flask that make it good at keeping hot liquids hot.

11) Do animals that live in hot climates tend to have large or small ears? Give one reason why this might be an advantage in a hot climate.

12)*If it costs £4000 to double glaze your house and the double glazing saves you £100 on energy bills every year, calculate the payback time for double glazing.

13) Name three ways of improving energy efficiency in the home. Explain how each improvement reduces the amount of heat lost from a house.

14) What can you tell from a material's U-value?

15)*An ornament has a mass of 0.5 kg. The ornament is made from a material that has a specific heat capacity of 1000 J/kg°C. How much energy does it take to heat the ornament from 20 °C to 200 °C?

16) Do heaters use materials that have a high or low heat capacity?

17) Name nine types of energy and give an example of each.

18) State the principle of the conservation of energy.

19) List the energy transformations that occur in a battery-powered toy car.

20)*What is the efficiency of a motor that converts 100 J of electrical energy into 70 J of useful kinetic energy?

21)*The following energy transformation diagram shows how energy is converted in a catapult.

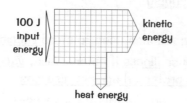

a) How much energy is converted into kinetic energy?
b) How much energy is wasted?
c) What is the efficiency of the catapult?

22) What is the equation for energy transferred by an electrical appliance?

23)*Calculate how many kWh of electrical energy are used by a 0.5 kW heater used for 15 minutes.

24) Would a battery-powered radio or a wind-up radio be more suitable to use if you were stranded on a desert island? Why?

Physics 1a — Energy

Energy Sources & Power Stations

There are <u>11</u> different types of <u>energy resource</u>. They fit into <u>two types</u>: <u>renewable</u> and <u>non-renewable</u>.

Non-Renewable Energy Resources Will Run Out One Day

The <u>non-renewables</u> are the <u>three FOSSIL FUELS</u> and <u>NUCLEAR</u>:

1) <u>Coal</u>   3) <u>Natural gas</u>

2) <u>Oil</u>   4) <u>Nuclear fuels</u> (<u>uranium</u> and <u>plutonium</u>)

a) They will <u>all 'run out'</u> one day.

b) They all do <u>damage</u> to the environment.

c) But they provide <u>most of our energy</u>.

Renewable Energy Resources Will Never Run Out

The <u>renewables</u> are:

1) <u>Wind</u>   5) <u>Solar</u>

2) <u>Waves</u>   6) <u>Geothermal</u>

3) <u>Tides</u>   7) <u>Biofuels</u>

4) <u>Hydroelectric</u>

a) These will <u>never run out</u>.

b) Most of them do <u>damage to the environment</u>, but <u>less damage</u> than non-renewables.

c) The trouble is they currently <u>don't provide as much energy</u> as the non-renewables.

d) Some of them <u>don't always work</u> because they depend on the <u>weather</u>.

Energy Sources can be Burnt to Drive Turbines in Power Stations

1) Almost <u>all</u> fossil-fuel (<u>coal</u>, <u>oil</u> and <u>gas</u>) <u>power stations</u> work in the <u>same</u> way.

2) The <u>fuel</u> (the energy source) is <u>burnt</u> to <u>heat water</u> (or <u>air</u> in some fossil-fuel power stations) to produce <u>steam</u>.

3) The <u>steam</u> drives (turns) a <u>turbine</u>.

4) The <u>turbine</u> is coupled (joined) to a <u>generator</u>. When the turbine <u>turns</u>, the <u>generator</u> produces <u>electricity</u>.

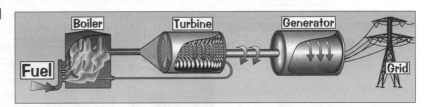

Nuclear Reactors are Just Fancy Boilers

1) A <u>nuclear power station</u> is almost the same as the one above.

2) Instead of burning fuel, a reaction called <u>nuclear fission</u> is used to <u>heat</u> water to make <u>steam</u> to drive <u>turbines</u>, etc. This means the <u>boiler</u> has to be slightly different.

3) Nuclear power stations take the <u>longest</u> time of all the power stations to <u>start up</u>.

4) <u>Natural-gas</u> power stations take the <u>shortest</u> time of all the <u>fossil-fuel</u> power stations.

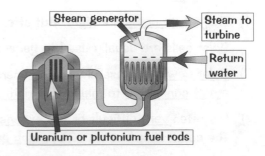

It all boils down to steam...

All power stations work in pretty much the <u>same way</u> — they just have slightly different ways of <u>turning a turbine</u>. Make sure you know how a standard power station works — it could earn you some juicy marks in the exam.

Renewable Energy Sources

Renewable energy sources will not run out. What's more, they do a lot less damage to the environment. Yay.

Wind Power — Lots of Little Wind Turbines

1) Windmills (wind turbines) are usually put up in windy places like on moors or round coasts.

2) Electricity is generated directly from the wind — the wind turns the blades, which turn the generator inside the wind turbine.

3) They don't release any harmful gases into the atmosphere. There are also no waste materials made.

4) But they do cause visual pollution (they spoil the view).

5) And they can be very noisy, which can be annoying for people living nearby.

6) Some people are worried that they can harm wildlife, e.g. birds.

7) There's also the problem that you can't make electricity when the wind stops.

8) The start-up costs are quite high, but there are no fuel costs and they're cheap to run.

9) You can use smaller turbines to generate electricity on a small scale, e.g. to power an office.

Solar Cells — Expensive but Don't Damage the Environment

1) Solar cells generate electric currents directly from sunlight.

2) There's no pollution — they don't produce any harmful gases or waste. (Except when they're made.)

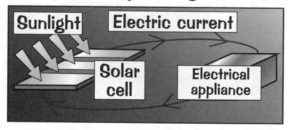

3) In sunny countries solar power is a very reliable source of energy (we can be pretty sure it will provide us with energy) — but only in the daytime.

4) The set-up costs are high. But after that the energy is free and running costs almost nothing.

5) Solar cells are usually used to generate electricity on a small scale, e.g. powering a house or calculators.

6) Solar power is a useful way to generate electricity in remote places which aren't connected to mains electricity, e.g. to power electric road signs.

7) It's often very difficult or too expensive to connect places that use solar panels to the National Grid. The connection cost is often much greater than the electricity they produce is worth.

This is true for any small scale production of electricity.

People love the idea of wind power — just not in their backyard...

You might not be able to power the country using solar cells, but they're great for powering smaller stuff. You can even get rucksacks with built-in solar cells to charge up your mobile phone while you walk. Pretty cool, huh.

Renewable Energy Sources

Wherever water is <u>moving</u>, we can use it to turn turbines and produce <u>electrical energy</u>.

Hydroelectric Power Uses Falling Water

1) <u>Water</u> is trapped by a <u>dam</u>, and is then allowed out to fall <u>through turbines</u>. As per usual, the turbines are coupled to a <u>generator</u>. As the turbines turn, electricity is produced.

2) No gases are released into the atmosphere when the electricity is generated. There are also <u>no waste materials</u>. But they can look <u>ugly</u> (visual pollution).

3) Some <u>wildlife</u> may also lose their <u>habitats</u> (where they live) when one of these power stations is built.

4) The really good thing about hydroelectric power is that it can produce electricity almost <u>as soon as you need it</u>, e.g. when <u>demand</u> for electricity is <u>high</u>. That's because you can <u>choose</u> when to <u>release</u> the water.

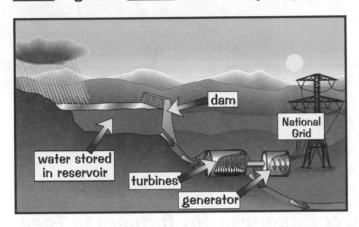

5) It's also a <u>very reliable way</u> of generating electricity (unless it <u>hasn't rained</u> for a long time).

6) Hydroelectric power stations are <u>expensive</u> to <u>set up</u>, but you <u>don't</u> need <u>any fuel</u>, and <u>running costs</u> are <u>low</u>.

7) It can be a useful way to generate electricity on a <u>small scale</u> in <u>remote areas</u>.

Pumped Storage Gives Extra Supply Just When It's Needed

1) Most large power stations have <u>huge boilers</u> which have to be kept running <u>all night</u> even though demand for electricity is <u>very low</u>. This means there's often <u>too much</u> electrical energy produced at night.

2) <u>Pumped storage</u> is one of the <u>best ways of storing</u> this energy.

3) In pumped storage, 'spare' <u>night-time electricity</u> is used to pump water up to a <u>higher reservoir</u>.

4) This can then be <u>released quickly</u> during periods of <u>high demand</u>.

5) Pumped storage <u>isn't</u> a way of <u>generating</u> power. It's simply a way of <u>storing energy</u> which has <u>already</u> been generated.

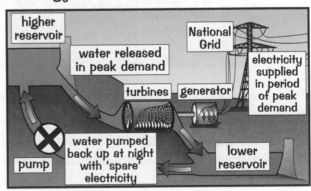

The hydroelectric power you're supplying — it's electrifying...

Hydroelectric power's great — it doesn't make any nasty gases and can give you electricity when everyone's crying out for it. Other than that it's the same old story — turn some turbines, generate some electricity. Learn it.

Renewable Energy Sources

It's easy to get confused between <u>wave power</u> and <u>tidal power</u> — but they are <u>completely different</u>.

Wave Power — Lots of Little Wave-Powered Turbines

1) As waves come in to the shore their <u>up and down motion</u> can be used to drive a <u>generator</u>.

2) They <u>don't</u> release any <u>harmful substances</u> into the atmosphere or any other <u>waste</u>.

3) They do <u>spoil the view</u>.

4) They are <u>fairly unreliable</u> — waves die out when the <u>wind drops</u>.

5) The <u>set up costs are high</u>, but there are <u>no fuel costs</u> and <u>very low running costs</u>.

6) Wave power isn't usually used to provide energy on a <u>large scale</u>, but it can be <u>very useful</u> on <u>small islands</u>.

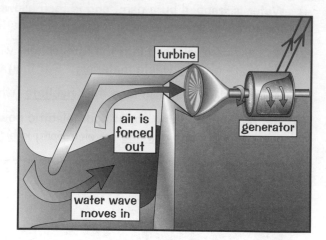

Tidal Barrages — Big Dams on River Estuaries with Turbines in Them

1) As the <u>tide comes in</u> it fills up the estuary and drives the <u>turbines</u>.

2) They <u>don't</u> produce any <u>harmful waste</u> — they <u>don't pollute</u> the atmosphere.

3) They do <u>spoil the view</u> — they create <u>visual pollution</u>.

4) They also <u>change</u> and <u>destroy the habitats</u> of some wildlife.

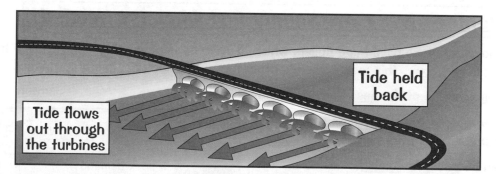

5) Tides are <u>reliable</u> — they happen <u>twice a day without fail</u>, and always near to the <u>predicted height</u>.

6) The <u>height</u> of the tides isn't always the same — lower tides will provide <u>a lot less energy</u> than the higher tides.

7) <u>Set up costs are quite high</u>, but there are <u>no fuel costs</u> and <u>very low running costs</u>.

8) Tidal power can be used to generate energy on a <u>large scale</u> (i.e. it can produce a <u>huge amount</u> of energy).

Learn about wave power — and bid your cares goodbye...

I do hope you appreciate the <u>big, big differences</u> between <u>tidal power</u> and <u>wave power</u>. They both involve salty seawater, sure — but that's the only thing that's the same really. Smile and enjoy. And <u>learn</u>.

Renewable Energy Sources

Well, who'd have guessed it — there's <u>yet more energy</u> lurking about in piles of rubbish and deep underground.

Geothermal Energy — Heat from Underground

1) In some <u>volcanic areas</u>, <u>steam</u> and <u>hot water</u> rise to the Earth's surface.

2) This steam can be used to drive a turbine which turns a <u>generator</u>.

3) This is actually <u>brilliant free energy</u> with no real environmental problems.

4) It <u>doesn't</u> produce <u>any pollution</u> or <u>waste</u>.

5) It shouldn't affect many <u>wildlife habitats</u>.

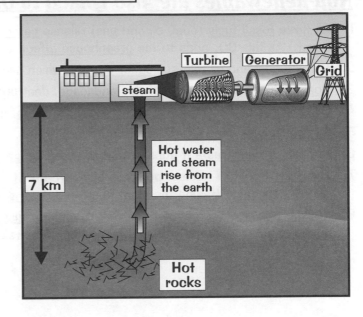

Biofuels are Made from Plants and Waste

1) Biofuels are <u>renewable energy resources</u>.

2) They're used to generate electricity in <u>exactly</u> the same way as fossil fuels — they're <u>burnt</u> to heat up <u>water</u> to produce <u>steam</u> to drive a <u>turbine</u>.

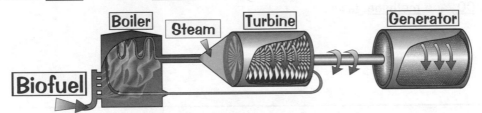

3) <u>Crops</u> like sugar cane can be fermented to produce <u>ethanol</u>, or plant oils can be changed to produce <u>biodiesel</u>.

4) Biofuels are quite <u>quick</u> and <u>cheap</u> to make.

Sugar cane to ethanol — a terrible waste in my opinion...

Why can't something more exciting than steam be made? Rabbits? Otters? Oh well. There might seem to be a lot to learn about energy sources, but don't panic. There are some things that are true for <u>all</u> of them, so you only have to learn them once, e.g. all the different ways of generating electricity are just different ways to <u>turn turbines</u>. Repeat with me: the steam/water drives the turbines connected to a generator, which produces electricity.

Energy Sources and the Environment

They might produce lots of energy, but using non-renewable energy sources and biofuels to generate electricity can have damaging effects on the environment. Read on...

Non-Renewables are Also Linked to Other Environmental Problems

1) All three fossil fuels (coal, oil and gas) release carbon dioxide (CO_2) into the atmosphere when they're burnt. All this CO_2 adds to the greenhouse effect, and contributes to global warming.

2) Burning coal and oil releases sulfur dioxide, which causes acid rain (which can harm plants and wildlife).

3) Coal mining makes a mess of the landscape, destroys wildlife habitats and creates visual pollution.

4) Oil spillages cause serious environmental problems, affecting creatures that live in and around the sea.

5) Nuclear power doesn't produce any harmful gases.

6) But the nuclear waste it does produce is very dangerous. It's very difficult to make safe and get rid of.

7) The overall cost of nuclear power is high. The cost of setting up the power plant and final decommissioning (taking the plant apart and dealing with any nuclear waste this creates) are both huge.

8) Nuclear power always carries the risk of a major disaster. If there's an explosion at the power plant, a lot of dangerous material could be released into the atmosphere.

Biofuels Have Their Disadvantages Too

1) The plants that grow to produce biofuels (or to feed the animals that produce the dung) take in carbon dioxide (CO_2) from the atmosphere as they grow.

2) When the biofuels are underline(burnt), this CO_2 is re-released into the atmosphere.

3) So the overall amount of CO_2 in the atmosphere stays the same.

4) In some regions, large areas of forest have been cleared to make room to grow biofuels, which causes lots of species to lose their natural habitats.

5) The rotting and burning of the plants from these forests also releases underline(CO_2) and methane gases.

Annual Pointing at Dung Competition

Carbon Capture can Reduce the Impact of Carbon Dioxide

1) Carbon capture and storage (CCS) is used to reduce the amount of CO_2 released into the atmosphere and help reduce the strength of the greenhouse effect.

2) CCS works by collecting the CO_2 from power stations before it is released into the atmosphere.

3) The captured CO_2 can then be pumped into empty gas fields and oil fields like those under the North Sea. It can be safely stored there without it adding to the greenhouse effect.

4) CCS is a new technology that's developing quickly. There might be loads of new and exciting ways to trap CO_2 just around the corner.

Empty oil and gas fields are just the empty holes underground left over when all the fuel has been removed.

Biofuels are great — but don't burn your biology notes just yet...

Wowsers. There certainly is a lot to bear in mind with all the different energy sources and all the good things and nasty things about them. The next page is really handy for comparing all the different energy sources...

Comparison of Energy Resources

Here's a nice summary of the good and bad points of all the different energy sources.
Learn 'em good.

Set-Up/Decommissioning (Shutdown) Time

1) These are both affected by the size of the power station and how complicated it is to design and build.

2) Planning issues can also add to the time it takes to set up a power station. E.g. talks over whether a nuclear power station should be built on a stretch of beautiful coastline can last years.

3) Gas power stations are the quickest of the fossil-fuel power stations to set up.

4) Nuclear power stations take by far the longest (and cost the most) to decommission.

Set-Up Costs

1) Renewable resources often need bigger power stations than non-renewables to produce the same amount of electricity

2) The bigger the power station, the more expensive it is to build.

3) Nuclear reactors and hydroelectric dams are huge and complicated to build. This means they're usually the most expensive.

Can we Rely on Them?

1) All the non-renewables are reliable energy sources (until they run out).

2) Many of the renewable sources depend on the weather. This means they're pretty unreliable here in the UK.

3) Tidal power, geothermal power and biofuels are all reliable (they don't depend on the weather).

Running/Fuel Costs

Renewables usually have the lowest running costs, because there's no actual fuel used.

Location Issues

A power station has to be near to the stuff it runs on.

Solar — pretty much anywhere, though the sunnier the better

Gas — pretty much anywhere there's piped gas (most of the UK)

Hydroelectric — hilly, rainy places with floodable valleys, e.g. the Lake District, Scottish Highlands

Wind — exposed, windy places like coasts or out at sea

Oil — near the coast (oil transported by sea)

Waves — on or near the coast

Coal — near coal mines, e.g. Yorkshire, Wales

Nuclear — away from people (in case of disaster), near water (for cooling)

Tidal — big river estuaries where a dam can be built

Geothermal — only in volcanic places

Environmental Issues

1) If there's a fuel involved, there will be waste pollution.

2) If it relies on the weather, it's often ugly and noisy.

Atmospheric Pollution
Coal, Oil, Gas,
(+ others, though less so).

Visual Pollution
Coal, Oil, Gas, Nuclear,
Tidal, Waves, Wind,
Hydroelectric.

Other Problems
Nuclear (dangerous waste, explosions),
Hydroelectric (dams bursting).

Using Up Resources
Coal, Oil, Gas, Nuclear.

Noise Pollution
Coal, Oil, Gas, Nuclear,
Wind.

Damages Wildlife Habitats
Hydroelectric, Tidal,
Biofuels.

Electricity and the National Grid

The <u>National Grid</u> is the <u>network</u> of pylons and cables that covers <u>the whole of Britain</u>, getting electricity to homes everywhere. Whoever you pay for your electricity, it's the National Grid that gets it to you.

Electricity is Distributed via the National Grid...

1) The <u>National Grid</u> takes electrical energy from <u>power stations</u> to where it's needed in <u>homes</u> and <u>industry</u>.

2) To transmit the <u>huge</u> amount of <u>power</u> needed, you need either a <u>high voltage</u> or a <u>high current</u>.

3) The <u>problem</u> with a <u>high current</u> is that you lose <u>loads of energy</u> through <u>heat</u> in the cables.

4) It's much <u>cheaper</u> to <u>boost the voltage</u> up <u>really high</u> (to 400 000 V) and keep the current <u>very low</u>.

'Distributed' is just a fancy way of saying the electricity is spread out and taken to where it's needed.

...With a Little Help from Pylons and Transformers

1) To get the voltage to 400 000 V to transmit power requires <u>transformers</u> as well as <u>big pylons</u>.

2) The <u>step-up transformers</u> are used to <u>increase</u> the voltage <u>up</u> to 400 000 V at one end.

3) It's then <u>reduced</u> again ('<u>stepped down</u>') to safe useable levels using a <u>step-down transformer</u>.

There are Different Ways to Transmit Electricity

1) Electrical energy can be moved around by cables <u>buried in the ground</u>, as well as in <u>overhead</u> power lines.

2) Each of these different options has its <u>pros and cons</u>:

	Set-up cost	Amount of looking after needed	Easy to get to if there's a problem?	How it looks	Affected by weather	Reliability	How easy to set up
Overhead Cables	lower	lots needed	yes	ugly	yes	less reliable	easy
Underground Cables	higher	not much	no	hidden	no	more reliable	hard

Supply and Demand

1) Our energy demands keep on <u>increasing</u>.

2) To meet these demands in the future, the <u>energy supplied</u> to the National Grid will need to <u>increase</u>, or the <u>energy demands</u> of consumers will need to <u>decrease</u>.

Transformers — NOT robots in disguise...

You don't need to know the <u>details</u> about exactly what transformers are and how they work — just that they increase and decrease the <u>voltage</u> to <u>minimise energy losses</u> in the National Grid.

Wave Basics

Waves transfer <u>energy</u> from one place to another.

Waves Have Amplitude, Wavelength and Frequency

1) The <u>amplitude</u> is the displacement (the shortest distance) from the <u>rest position</u> to the <u>crest</u> (NOT from a trough to a crest).

2) The <u>wavelength</u> is the length of a <u>full cycle</u> of the wave, e.g. from <u>crest to crest</u>.

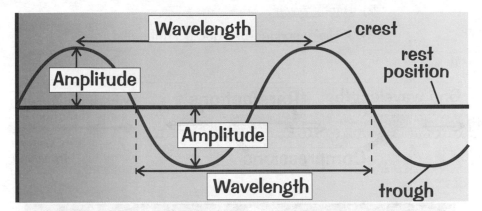

3) <u>Frequency</u> is the <u>number of complete waves</u> passing a certain point <u>per second</u> OR the <u>number of waves</u> produced by a source <u>each second</u>.

4) Frequency is measured in hertz (Hz). 1 Hz is <u>1 wave per second</u>.

Transverse Waves Have Sideways Vibrations

<u>Most waves</u> are <u>transverse</u>:

1) <u>Light</u> and <u>all other electromagnetic waves</u> (see p99).

2) A <u>slinky spring</u> wiggled up and down.

3) <u>Ripples</u> on water.

4) <u>Waves</u> on <u>strings</u>.

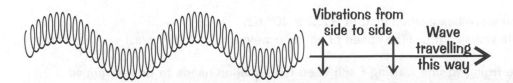

In <u>TRANSVERSE</u> waves the vibrations are <u>PERPENDICULAR</u> (at <u>90°</u>) to the <u>DIRECTION OF ENERGY TRANSFER</u> of the wave.

(i.e. the direction the wave is travelling)

There is <u>another type</u> of wave you need to know about — see the next page...

Waves — dig the vibes, man...

So make sure you know what is meant by the <u>amplitude</u>, <u>wavelength</u> and <u>frequency</u> of a wave. And know what a <u>transverse</u> wave is too. Then when you're happy with all that, take a look at the next page for more wave fun.

Wave Basics

There are <u>two</u> types of wave — you met transverse waves on the last page. Now here's <u>longitudinal</u> waves...

Longitudinal Waves Have Vibrations Along the Same Line

Examples of <u>longitudinal waves</u> are:

1) <u>Sound waves</u> and <u>ultrasound</u>.

2) <u>Shock waves</u>.

3) A <u>slinky spring</u> when you <u>push</u> the end.

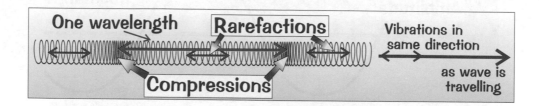

In <u>LONGITUDINAL</u> waves the vibrations are <u>PARALLEL</u> to the <u>DIRECTION OF ENERGY TRANSFER</u> of the wave.

Wave Speed = Frequency × Wavelength

The equation below applies to <u>all waves</u>. You need to learn it — and <u>practise using it</u>.

$$\text{Speed} = \text{Frequency} \times \text{Wavelength}$$
$$\text{(m/s)} \qquad \text{(Hz)} \qquad \text{(m)}$$

OR $v = f \times \lambda$

Wavelength (that's the Greek letter 'lambda')

Speed (v is for <u>velocity</u>) Frequency

<u>EXAMPLE:</u> A radio wave has a frequency of 92.2×10^6 Hz. Find its wavelength. (The speed of all radio waves is 3×10^8 m/s.)

<u>ANSWER:</u> You're trying to find λ using f and v, so the equation needs to be rearranged to give: $\lambda = v \div f$ (you won't need to rearrange any equations in the exam — those nice examiners will do it for you).

So $\lambda = v \div f = 3 \times 10^8 \div 9.22 \times 10^7 = \underline{3.25 \text{ m}}$.

Go on, be nice — give us a wave...

Learn the differences between longitudinal and transverse waves. Then practise using $\underline{v = f \times \lambda}$ with this question: A sound wave travelling in a solid has a frequency of $\underline{1.9 \times 10^4 \text{ Hz}}$ and a wavelength of $\underline{12.5 \text{ cm}}$. Find its speed.*

Physics 1b — Electricity and Waves

Wave Properties

If you're anything like me, you'll have spent hours gazing into a mirror in <u>wonder</u>. Here's why...

Reflection of Light Lets Us See Things

1) <u>Reflection of light</u> is what allows us to <u>see</u> objects. Light bounces off them into our eyes.

2) The <u>LAW OF REFLECTION</u> applies to <u>every reflected ray</u>:

> ### Angle of <u>INCIDENCE</u> = Angle of <u>REFLECTION</u>

3) Note that these two angles are <u>ALWAYS</u> measured between the ray itself and the <u>NORMAL</u>, shown dotted here.

4) The normal is just a <u>line</u> at <u>right angles</u> to the mirror where the incident ray hits it.

5) Whenever you're drawing <u>reflections</u> you need to make sure the <u>angle of incidence</u> and <u>angle of reflection</u> are the <u>same</u>...

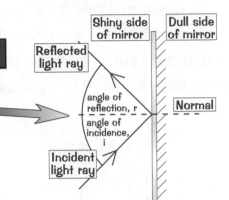

<u>EXAMPLE:</u> Ben uses a <u>mirror</u> at the side of the road to see cars coming from the <u>right</u> from his driveway. Complete the <u>ray diagram</u> to show how Ben in his <u>blue car</u> is able to see the <u>red car</u>.

<u>ANSWER:</u>

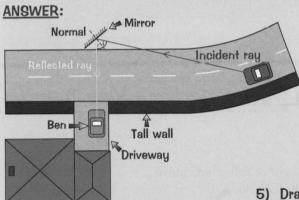

1) Draw an <u>incident ray</u> from the <u>red car</u> to centre of the <u>mirror</u>.

2) Draw a <u>normal</u>.

3) <u>Measure</u> the <u>angle of incidence</u>, <u>i</u> (the angle between the incident ray and the normal), using a protractor.

4) <u>Measure</u> and <u>mark</u> the <u>angle of reflection</u>, <u>r</u>, out on the <u>other side</u> of the normal. Remember, i = r.

5) Draw a <u>reflected ray</u> through your <u>mark</u> for <u>r</u> to the <u>blue car</u>.

An Image Formed in a Plane Mirror is Virtual and Upright

Learn these <u>four important points</u> for how an image is formed in a <u>plane mirror</u> (a mirror with a <u>flat</u> surface):

1) The <u>image</u> is the <u>same size</u> as the <u>object</u>.

2) It is <u>AS FAR BEHIND</u> the mirror as the object is <u>in front</u>.

3) The image is <u>VIRTUAL</u> (it <u>appears</u> to be coming from a completely <u>different place</u>) and <u>UPRIGHT</u>.

4) The image is <u>LATERALLY INVERTED</u> — the right side of the object appears to be left side of the image. Likewise, the left side of the object appears to be the right side of the image.

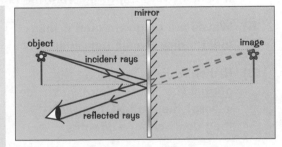

Plane mirrors — what pilots use to look behind them...

It's really important you don't forget the law of reflection: angle of incidence = angle of reflection. Make sure you know how to draw a nice, clear <u>ray diagram</u> too and you should be well on your way to a great mark.

Refraction and Diffraction

If you thought <u>reflection</u> was good, you'll just love <u>diffraction</u> and <u>refraction</u> — it's awesome. If you didn't find reflection interesting then I'm afraid it's tough luck — you need to know about <u>all three</u> of them. Sorry.

Diffraction — Waves Spreading Out

1) All waves <u>spread out</u> ('<u>diffract</u>') at the edges when they pass through a <u>gap</u> or <u>pass an object</u>.

2) The amount of diffraction depends on the size of the gap relative to the wavelength of the wave.

3) The <u>narrower the gap</u>, or the <u>longer the wavelength</u>, the <u>more</u> the wave spreads out.

4) A <u>narrow gap</u> is one about the same <u>order of magnitude</u> (size) as the <u>wavelength</u> of the wave.

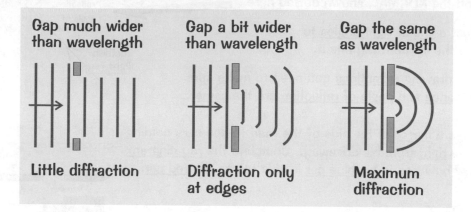

Refraction — Waves Changing Direction When Entering a New Material

1) When a wave crosses an interface (boundary) between two substances (from glass to air, say) it <u>changes direction</u>.

2) When light shines on a glass <u>window pane</u>, some of the light is reflected, but a lot of it passes through the glass and gets <u>refracted</u> as it does so:

3) As the light passes from the air into the glass it bends ('refracts') <u>towards</u> the normal.

4) When the light reaches the 'glass to air' boundary on the other side of the window, it bends (refracts) <u>away</u> from the normal.

5) Waves are <u>only</u> refracted if they meet a new medium <u>at an angle</u>.

6) If they're travelling <u>along the normal</u> (i.e. the angle of incidence is zero) they are <u>NOT refracted</u> — they don't change direction.

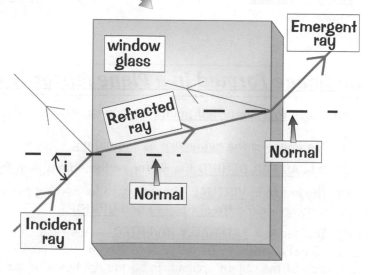

Lights, camera, refraction...

Diffraction's not too hard to get to grips with — especially if you can <u>remember those diagrams</u> at the top of the page. Also remember that <u>all</u> waves can be <u>diffracted</u> — so it doesn't matter if they're <u>longitudinal</u> or <u>transverse</u>.

EM Waves and Communication

Types of electromagnetic (EM) wave have a lot in common with one another, but their differences make them useful to us in different ways. These pages are packed with loads of important information, so pay attention...

There are Seven Types of EM Wave

1) EM waves with different wavelengths (or frequencies) have different properties.

2) We group them into seven basic types of EM wave.

3) They form a continuous spectrum (this means there are no gaps between each type of EM wave).

4) They're shown below increasing in frequency and energy (decreasing wavelength) from left to right.

RADIO WAVES	MICRO-WAVES	INFRA-RED	VISIBLE LIGHT	ULTRA-VIOLET	X-RAYS	GAMMA RAYS
$1\ m - 10^4\ m$	$10^{-2}\ m\ (1\ cm)$	$10^{-5}\ m\ (0.01\ mm)$	$10^{-7}\ m$	$10^{-8}\ m$	$10^{-10}\ m$	$10^{-12}\ m - 10^{-15}\ m$

wavelength →

5) All the different types of EM wave travel at the same speed in a vacuum (e.g. space).

6) The wavelengths of EM waves vary from 10^{-15} m (gamma rays) to more than 10^4 m (radio waves).

7) EM waves with higher frequencies have shorter wavelengths.

8) Because of their different properties, different EM waves are used for different purposes.

9) EM waves have different uses for communication (transferring information) because of their different wavelengths.

Radio Waves are Used Mainly for Communication

1) Long-wave radio can be sent and received halfway round the world.

2) That's because long wavelengths diffract (bend, see p.98) around the curved surface of the Earth. They also get around hills and into tunnels.

3) This diffraction effect makes it possible for radio signals to be received even if the receiver isn't in the line of sight of the transmitter.

4) The radio waves used for TV and FM radio transmissions have very short wavelengths.

5) To receive TV and FM signals, there must be nothing between the aerial and the transmitter — the signal doesn't bend around hills or travel far through buildings.

6) Short-wave radio signals can, like long-wave, be received at long distances from the transmitter.

7) That's because they are reflected by the Earth's upper atmosphere.

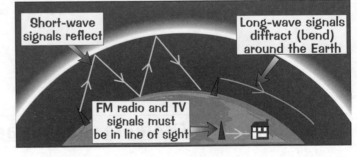

Short-wave signals reflect

Long-wave signals diffract (bend) around the Earth

FM radio and TV signals must be in line of sight

Size matters — and my wave's longer than yours...

You'll have to be able to name the order of the different types of EM waves in terms of their energy, frequency and wavelength. To remember the order of increasing frequency and energy, I use: **R**ock **M**usic **I**s **V**ery **U**seful for e**X**periments with **G**oats. It sounds stupid but it does work — why not make up your own...

EM Waves and Their Uses

Radio waves aren't the only waves used for communication — other EM waves come in <u>pretty handy</u> too.

Microwaves are Used for Satellite Communication and Mobile Phones

1) For satellite TV, the signal from a <u>transmitter</u> is transmitted into space...

2) ... where it's picked up by the satellite's receiver dish.

3) The satellite <u>transmits</u> the signal back to Earth in a different direction...

4) ... where it's received by a <u>satellite dish</u> on the ground.

5) Mobile phone calls also travel as <u>microwaves</u> between your phone and the nearest <u>transmitter</u>.

6) Microwaves are used by <u>remote-sensing</u> satellites — to 'see' through the clouds, e.g. to monitor oil spills.

Some wavelengths of microwaves are <u>absorbed</u> by <u>water</u> molecules and <u>heat</u> them up. If the water happens to be in <u>your cells</u>, you might start to <u>cook</u>. Some people think using your mobile a lot (especially next your <u>head</u>), or living near a <u>mast</u>, could damage your <u>health</u>. There isn't any <u>proof</u> either way yet.

Infrared Waves are Used for Remote Controls

1) <u>Infrared</u> waves are used in lots of <u>wireless remote controllers</u>.

2) Remote controls work by <u>emitting</u> different <u>patterns</u> of infrared waves to send <u>different instructions</u> to an appliance, e.g. a TV.

Visible Light is Useful for Photography

1) Cameras use a <u>lens</u> to focus <u>visible light</u> onto a light-sensitive <u>film</u> or electronic <u>sensor</u>.

2) The lens <u>aperture</u> (opening) controls <u>how much</u> light enters the camera.

3) The <u>shutter speed</u> allows you to control <u>how long</u> the film or sensor is <u>open</u> to the light.

4) The <u>longer</u> the film or sensor is <u>open</u> to the light — the <u>more light</u> that will enter the camera and react with the film.

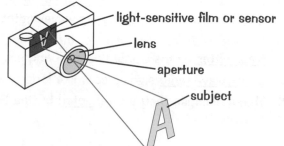

Microwaves are also used for making popcorn — mmm...

In the exam, you might be asked how each of these waves can be used in <u>communications</u>. Remember all the <u>lovely examples</u> on this page to pick up lots of wave-tastic marks.

Sound Waves

We hear sounds after <u>vibrations</u> reach our <u>eardrums</u>. You'll need to know how sound waves work.

Sound Travels as a Wave

1) <u>Sound waves</u> are caused by <u>vibrating objects</u>.

2) These vibrations are passed through the surrounding medium (substance, e.g. air) as a series of <u>compressions</u> (squashed up bits).

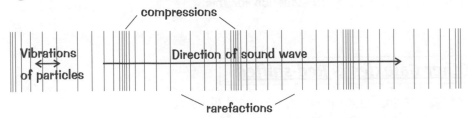

3) Sound waves are a type of <u>longitudinal wave</u> (see page 96).

4) Sometimes the sound will eventually travel into someone's <u>ear</u>, at which point the person might <u>hear it</u>.

5) Sound can't travel in <u>space</u>, because it's mostly a <u>vacuum</u> (there are no particles).

Sound Waves Can Reflect and Refract

1) Sound waves will be <u>reflected</u> by <u>hard flat surfaces</u>.

2) <u>Echoes</u> are just <u>reflected</u> sound waves.

3) You hear a <u>delay</u> between the <u>original</u> sound and the <u>echo</u> because the echoed sound waves have to <u>travel further</u>, and so take <u>longer</u> to reach your ears.

4) <u>Sound waves</u> will also refract (see p98).

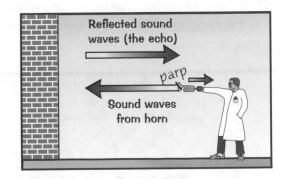

The Higher the Frequency, the Higher the Pitch

1) <u>High frequency</u> sound waves sound <u>high pitched</u> like a <u>squeaking mouse</u>.

2) <u>Low frequency</u> sound waves sound <u>low pitched</u> like a <u>mooing cow</u>.

3) <u>Frequency</u> is the number of <u>complete vibrations</u> each second — so a wave that has a frequency of 100 Hz vibrates 100 times each second.

4) Common <u>units</u> are <u>kHz</u> (1000 Hz).

5) <u>High frequency</u> (or high pitch) also means <u>shorter wavelength</u> (see page 95).

6) The <u>loudness</u> of a sound depends on the <u>amplitude</u> of the sound wave.

7) A <u>higher amplitude</u> means a <u>louder sound</u>.

Hello, hello, hello — it's very echoey on this page, this page, this page...

The thing to do here is learn the facts. There's a simple equation that says <u>the more you learn now</u>, the <u>more marks you'll get</u> in the exam. A lot of questions just test whether you've learnt the facts. Easy marks, really.

The Origin of the Universe

OK. Let's not kid ourselves — this is a pretty <u>scary</u> topic. How the universe <u>started</u> is a <u>BIG</u> question. But <u>looking</u> at <u>stars</u> and <u>galaxies</u> might <u>help</u> us answer that question...

The Universe Seems to be Expanding

1) As big as the universe already is, it looks like it's getting <u>even bigger</u>.

2) All its <u>galaxies</u> seem to be moving away from each other (apart from a few very close ones). There's good evidence for this...

1) Light from Other Galaxies is Red-shifted

1) When we look at <u>light from distant galaxies</u> we see it at <u>longer wavelengths</u> (and lower frequencies) than it should be.

2) The light is shifted towards the <u>red end</u> of the electromagnetic spectrum. This is called <u>red-shift</u>.

3) It's the same effect as the vrrroomm from a racing car — the engine sounds <u>lower-pitched</u> when the car's gone past you and is <u>moving away</u> from you. This is called the <u>Doppler effect</u>.

THE DOPPLER EFFECT

1) When something that emits waves moves <u>towards</u> you or <u>away</u> from you, the <u>wavelengths</u> and <u>frequencies</u> of the waves seem <u>different</u> — compared to when the source of the waves is <u>stationary</u>.

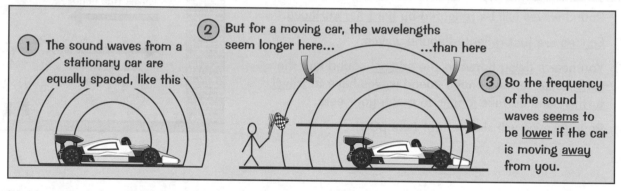

1) The sound waves from a stationary car are equally spaced, like this

2) But for a moving car, the wavelengths seem longer here... ...than here

3) So the frequency of the sound waves <u>seems</u> to be <u>lower</u> if the car is moving <u>away</u> from you.

2) The <u>frequency</u> of a source moving <u>towards</u> you will seem <u>higher</u> and its <u>wavelength</u> will seem <u>shorter</u>.

3) The Doppler effect happens to both <u>longitudinal</u> waves (e.g. sound) and <u>transverse</u> waves (e.g. light and microwaves).

2) The Further Away a Galaxy is, the Greater the Red-shift

1) <u>Measurements</u> of the red-shift suggest that <u>all the galaxies</u> (apart from a few close ones) are <u>moving away from us</u> very quickly...

2) ...and it's the <u>same result</u> whichever direction you look in.

3) <u>More distant</u> galaxies have <u>greater</u> red-shifts than nearer ones.

4) This means that more distant galaxies are <u>moving away</u> from us <u>faster</u> than nearer ones.

5) This is evidence that the whole universe is <u>expanding</u>.

If a tree falls down in the forest and you're driving away from it...

Listen out for the Doppler effect next time you hear a fast <u>motorbike</u> or a police <u>siren</u>. Remember, red-shift gives us evidence that the universe is <u>expanding</u> — as it shows all the galaxies seem to be <u>moving away</u> from us.

The Origin of the Universe

Once upon a time there was a really <u>Big Bang</u> — that's the <u>best theory</u> we've got.

It All Started Off with a Very Big Bang (Probably)

1) If distant galaxies are moving <u>away</u> from us then something must have <u>got them going</u>.

2) That 'something' was probably a <u>big explosion</u> — so they called it the <u>Big Bang</u>...

3) According to the Big Bang theory, all the matter and energy in the universe must have been packed into a <u>very small space</u>.

4) Then it <u>exploded</u> from that single point and started expanding.

5) The <u>expansion</u> is still going on.

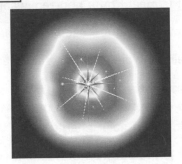

There's Microwave Radiation Coming from All Directions

1) Scientists have detected <u>low frequency electromagnetic radiation</u> coming from <u>all parts</u> of the universe.

2) This radiation is largely in the <u>microwave</u> part of the EM spectrum.

3) It's known as the <u>cosmic microwave background radiation</u> (CMBR).

4) The <u>Big Bang theory</u> is the <u>only</u> theory that can explain the CMBR.

5) The CMBR comes from radiation that was around shortly after the <u>beginning</u> of the universe.

The Big Bang Theory Has Its Limitations

1) The Big Bang theory <u>isn't perfect</u> — there are some observations that the theory can't yet explain.

2) For example, the Big Bang theory predicts that the universe's expansion should be <u>slowing down</u> — but as far as we can tell it's actually <u>speeding up</u>.

3) It also doesn't explain what actually <u>caused</u> the explosion in the first place. Or what things were like <u>before</u> the explosion (or if there was a 'before').

4) But even though the Big Bang theory <u>doesn't</u> answer all our questions, it won't just be <u>dumped</u>.

5) It's more likely that scientists will <u>make changes</u> to the theory so that it works better. As it's the <u>best</u> theory that we've got to explain how the universe began.

Time and space — it's funny old stuff, isn't it...

<u>Proving</u> a scientific theory is impossible. If enough evidence points a certain way, then a theory can look pretty <u>believable</u>. But that doesn't <u>prove</u> it's a <u>fact</u> — <u>new evidence</u> may change people's minds.

Revision Summary for Physics 1b

It's business time. Do as many of the questions as you can and then try the tricky ones after you've had another chance to read the pages you struggled on.

1) What is meant by a non-renewable energy resource? Name four different non-renewable energy resources.

2) What two fuels are used in nuclear power?

3) Explain how electricity is generated in a gas-fired power station.

4) Describe how the following renewable resources are used to generate electricity.
   State one advantage and one disadvantage for each resource.
   a) wind   b) solar energy   c) the tide   d) waves   e) geothermal energy

5) What is the purpose of pumped storage?

6) How are biofuels produced?

7) Name one place that carbon dioxide can be stored after carbon capture.

8) Name six things that should be thought about when a new power station is being planned.

9) Which three energy sources are linked most strongly with habitat disruption?

10) Explain why a very high electrical voltage is used to transmit electricity in the National Grid.

11) What are transformers used for?

12) Draw a diagram to illustrate frequency, wavelength and amplitude.

13)* Find the speed of a wave with frequency 50 kHz and wavelength 0.3 cm.

14) a) Sketch a diagram of a ray of light being reflected in a mirror.
    b) Label the normal and the angles of incidence and reflection.

15) What is refraction?

16) Sketch the EM spectrum with all its details. Put the lowest frequency waves on the left.

17) Why can't sound waves travel in space?

18) Are high frequency sound waves high pitched or low pitched?

19) If a wave source is moving towards you, will the observed frequency
    of its waves be higher or lower than their actual frequency?

20) What do red-shift observations tell us about the universe?

21) Describe the 'Big Bang' theory for the origin of the universe. What evidence is there for this theory?

The Perfect Cup of Tea

The making and drinking of tea are important life skills. It's not something that will crop up in the exam, but it is something that will make your revision much easier. So here's a guide to making the perfect cuppa...

1) Choose the Right Mug

A good mug is an essential part of the tea drinking experience, but choosing the right vessel for your tea can be tricky. Here's a guide to choosing your mug:

Some bad mugs:

No handles.

Too fancy (and saucers are for grannies).

Too flimsy and too 80s.

Too many handles.

The perfect mug:

Holds just the right amount of tea.

Wide enough to dunk a biscuit.

Has a design that complements your personality (yes, I'm a bit hippy).

Nice, easy to hold handle.

2) Get Some Water and Boil It

For a really great brew follow these easy step-by-step instructions:

1) First, pour some water into a kettle and switch it on. (Check it's switched on at the wall too.)

2) Let the kettle boil. While you're waiting, see what's on TV later and check your belly button for fluff. Oh, and put a tea bag in a mug.

3) Once the kettle has boiled, pour the water into the mug.

4) Mash the tea bag about a bit with a spoon. Remove the tea bag.

5) Add a splash of milk (and a lump of sugar or two if you're feeling naughty).

Top tea tip no. 23: why not ask your mum if she wants a cup too?

Note: some people may tell you to add the milk before the tea. Scientists have recently confirmed that this is nonsense.

3) Sit Back and Relax

Now this is important — once you've made your cuppa:

1) Have a quick rummage in the kitchen cupboards for a cheeky biscuit. (Custard creams are best — steer clear of any ginger biscuits — they're evil.)

2) Find your favourite armchair/beanbag. Move the cat.

3) Sit back and enjoy your mug of tea. You've earned it.

Phew — time for a brew I reckon...

It's best to ignore what other people say about making cups of tea and follow this method. Trust me, this is the most definitive and effective method. If you don't do it this way, you'll have a shoddy drinking experience. There, you've been warned. Now go and get the kettle on. Mine's milk and two sugars...

Index

Index

Index

Answers

Revision Summary for Biology 1a (page 29)

2) A professional runner (because they have a more active job).

13) a) Response A   b) Response B

Revision Summary for Chemistry 1a (page 61)

3) Calcium

6) a) top left
   b) bottom right

Revision Summary for Chemistry 1b (page 71)

16) b) 3.5 years

Efficiency of Machines Top Tip (page 81)
Loudspeaker: 0.0143 or 1.43%

Revision Summary for Physics 1a (page 86)

12) 40 years

15) 90 kJ

20) 0.7 or 70%

21) a) 80 J   b) 20 J   c) 0.8 or 80%

23) 0.125 kWh

Wave Basics Top Tip (page 96)
2735 m/s

Revision Summary for Physics 1b (page 104)

13) 150 m/s